Life After Miscarriage

Your Guide to Healing From Pregnancy Loss

D1258641

Jo Tocher

Disclaimer

Dedicated To

Baby John who, without his short incarnation of 24 weeks, this book wouldn't have been written and my journey would have been very different. Thank you for the life lessons I have learnt and for showing me what love is.

This book is also dedicated to John Tocher, my father, who died during my time writing it. Thank you for being the solid rock in my life, for showing me integrity, security, unconditional love and for allowing me to experience grief in a different way.

Table of Contents

Preface

I never in a million years thought I'd be writing a book. I had decided I wasn't an author or a writer.

When I found myself in flow with my passion and purpose (and I can tell you that took some finding) it was when, in the words of Brené Brown, the universe was gently tapping me on my shoulder, whispering the time was now. If not now, when? It's a bit of a wake-up call when you reach fifty—you realise time isn't infinite.

So, I found myself booking a 'Retreat to Write' on the Sunshine Coast, Australia with Emily Gowor, an extraordinary, inspirational writing coach. The very words 'Sunshine Coast' after a long, hard British winter was the catalyst. I just knew I had to be there; I had a message to share and I wanted to serve the thousands of women who had suffered miscarriage and pregnancy loss. We are one in four and too many of us are left to flounder and heal mostly on our own.

I had to overcome my mindset that I wasn't a writer—who was I to say I couldn't write? We all have a story and a heart to share it from. Writing from the heart is powerful and here I am opening my heart to the world, sharing my story in the hope that it will inspire you to heal, to realise that you're not alone and to begin to move forward so you can live your life fully.

"It took me quite a long time to develop a voice, and now that I have it, I am not going to be silent."

— *Madeleine Albright*

Introduction

This book has been written for women who have lost a baby in pregnancy, whether it is an early miscarriage, missed miscarriage, blighted ovum, recurrent miscarriage, ectopic pregnancy, late miscarriage or a stillbirth. Whether you have had one or more of these, the emotional pain and grief you are feeling can be overwhelming. You feel like you don't know what to do with yourself or your pain. You can't even imagine what it's like to feel normal again and it seems like no one understands what you are going through. You feel totally alone.

You feel the pain of loss, the pain of what might have been, the dreams that were shattered and lost but never forgotten.

I wrote this book because I have been there and I know what it feels like. I felt lost and isolated in my grief. I didn't want to talk about it and I pretended that I was fine but really, I wanted to talk about it with someone who understood and had been there. So, this book is written for those of you who are ready to heal from the trauma of pregnancy loss in a holistic, energetic, psychological and physical way. We are mind, body, soul and energy which all needs nourishing and healing after such a trauma.

This book is also written for those who have a loved one, a friend, a sister or a family member who is suffering from this silent grief. Reading this will help you understand what they are going through so you can support them and empathise fully.

Together we will explore the emotions you are feeling and the impact of miscarriage on your relationships with your partner, your friends and your family. We will also look at some coping strategies you may use as a default and some helpful techniques to get you through each day.

You will learn you can recover and move on but never forget because that baby is part of you and always will be. You will feel lighter and supported as I share with you my tips and techniques I've learnt over the past twenty years as a holistic therapist. It may even inspire you to nourish your soul and listen to the whispers of your heart, to find your passion and purpose which lights you up.

I was inspired to write this book because miscarriage is a silent pain; one that is often swept under the carpet and not spoken of. When it is spoken of, it is mentioned briefly then the silence steps in. It's for those women who find it keeps bubbling up, those women who know it is still unresolved and those women who would love to let go of the pain they've been carrying in their hearts. It's for the women who have recently lost and the women who have lost many years ago. There was nothing available to me during my time of loss and I would have loved to have quietly read a self-help book, at my own pace and in my own time. This is my contribution to all of you who have carried, loved and lost. To those of you who are feeling alone and sad, desperate to know what you can do to feel better. It is a culmination of the many courses I've completed over the past twenty years put together to help you.

It's my way of reaching out and leaving a small legacy to help you through this difficult time. It's my hope that you will come out feeling stronger; that you find peace, acceptance and begin to feel hopeful for your future.

My Story

I was happily working in the City of London, in the business development department organising business travel, exhibitions and conferences. It was a great job and I loved it. I had fun colleagues, we worked hard and had a good time socially with lots of in-house parties and drinks after work. I remember feeling unwell for several weeks when a friend and colleague suggested I might be pregnant. We went out in the lunch break and bought a pregnancy kit and I did the test in the bathroom at work—not the best idea when you have to get back and do an afternoon's work. I was stunned and shocked and really don't know how I got through the afternoon. I was living with my partner and we hadn't discussed marriage or children, it just hadn't come up. When I told him that evening he was also shocked, we talked it through and decided to continue with the pregnancy. We announced it to family, who were also a bit surprised since it wasn't normal to have a baby out of wedlock. I was in my thirties at the time, so I didn't want to waste the opportunity of having a baby.

We went to the twelve-week scan and all was well, but because of my age, we were encouraged to have an amniocentesis to detect for Down syndrome, which we did. At about twenty-three weeks, I went alone to get the test results and have a further scan. It was at this scan that I knew something wasn't right. The sonographer went quiet and was staring intently at the screen. She then left the room saying she'd be back soon. I was left lying there wondering, waiting and feeling an intense sensation of dread. Eventually, she came back with a doctor to have another look and it was then I found out that the baby wasn't forming correctly. There was amniotic fluid in the baby's stomach. The results weren't good; we had to decide to terminate or let nature take its course. The following day my partner came back to the hospital with me and we decided to let nature take its course and go home. We were to return after the weekend to see what the situation was.

By the time we returned, our baby had died and the bottom had fallen out of our world. I had to return to deliver my dead baby boy, one of the most traumatic events I have ever experienced. The midwife was helpful and it can't have been easy for her either. I was lucky enough to have a friend who offered to come with me to the birth. She was an ex-nurse and her medical knowledge was very helpful at the time, as well as her moral support. After the birth, they asked if I wanted to hold my baby boy and I just couldn't because I didn't think I'd ever let go. They placed him in a blanket on top of me before taking him away and also took photos of him, and gave me ink prints of his feet and hands. That was our momento; it was something to take away. That night, I was put on the ward with other mothers who were waiting to have babies and luckily I was in a side room. The nurse on duty was a beautiful, softly spoken Caribbean woman, who was the first person to tell me how sorry she was for my loss. At this point, the floodgates opened and I was inconsolable, but at the same time I was determined to keep it together, so I repressed my grief. 'Keep calm and carry on, don't make a fuss.'

I was offered counselling by the hospital, which I accepted but found to be ineffectual as it was just too early and I really didn't want to talk about it. The hospital chaplain visited and suggested we have a non-denominational funeral service. This again was something I couldn't bear the thought of, so turned it down. However, he was rather persistent and advised us to go ahead saying this would help with the healing cycle. It is something that I now recommend to my clients as it helps with closure. I wrote a beautiful poem to my baby John (we decided to name him after my father). The chaplain was very inspiring and supportive and it was a beautiful thing to do. After the service, the chaplain took us to a local cemetery to bury him. That tiny coffin was a heartbreaker; an image I'll never forget or get over. We decided to have a post-mortem because I really wanted to know what had happened. The results came back some time later with the conclusion that I had contracted a virus (Cytomegalovirus) which can affect the foetal development. I was one of the unlucky ones.

I decided to write this book to help others heal from the trauma of baby loss, as there just wasn't enough support for me at the time, and from what my clients tell me there's not much more available now. You're just sent home after your traumatic event, feeling lost and alone and traumatised. There are so many emotions coursing around and you have no idea how to deal with them and what to tackle first. So, you flounder for a bit, trying to keep yourself together, with a million questions running around your head. Why did this happen to me? What went wrong? When did it go wrong? How long had the baby not been developing properly? When will the pain go away? Your life as you knew it has been turned upside down—you'll never be the same.

The loss of my baby changed me. Everything was different from there on, intrinsically my soul had changed and it was crying out for change. During this time I had my biggest lightbulb moment. My corporate job seemed meaningless, the Chief

Executive's goals were not mine, they were his, and I didn't want to be a part of it anymore. I felt driven to go out and make change for the better; only at this point, I had no idea what to do and how to do it. This was the Universe's way of giving me an almighty kick up the backside, to get out and be a change maker and to make a difference in the world.

Eventually (it took about eighteen months), I found my thing and it came to me as I was flicking through a magazine. I read an article about a woman who had left her corporate career because she wasn't fulfilled anymore and trained to become an aromatherapist at the world famous Tisserand Institute in London. The hairs began to rise on the back of my neck and I just knew this was for me. I booked a taster weekend and absolutely loved it, and decided to sign up for a diploma course: The Tisserand Institute Diploma of Holistic Aromatherapy (TIDHA). This was the beginning of my journey with holistic therapy and other healing modalities, which led me to help thousands of women release the grief of miscarriage and come to a place of hope and reconciliation with themselves. In this book, I share some of the methods I've learnt over the past twenty years as a holistic therapist, wellbeing coach and miscarriage mentor.

"If there ever comes a day when we can't be together, keep me in your heart, I'll stay there forever."

—*Winnie the Pooh, A. A. Milne*

Chapter 1: The Pain of Loss

Miscarriage affects one in four women. Bearing in mind there are approximately 32 million women in the UK alone, which leaves around 11 million of childbearing age, suggesting 2.75 million women in the UK who have lost a baby during pregnancy. What a mind-blowing statistic.

Early miscarriage is pregnancy loss that occurs during the first trimester of Pregnancy and accounts for approximately 80% of all miscarriages. The earliest of miscarriages occur before the fertilised egg has implanted within the endometrium - the tissue lining of the womb. The woman may not realise she has had a loss as the small bleed is likely to occur around the time of her usual monthly period. It is quite common for the immune system to perceive an embryo as a foreign body even if it is healthy and the body discharges it.

A **Missed Miscarriage** or Silent Miscarriage as it is sometimes known, is usually detected at the 12-week scan when it's discovered there is no heart beat. The embryo and sac are still attached but the foetus has stopped developing for some reason, usually down to chromosomal irregularities.

A **Blighted Ovum**, is when a fertilised egg (ovum) implants in the Uterus, without any development or growth. However the pregnancy sac continues to grow and the mother still feels pregnant. It is usually detected by scan during 8-13 weeks . It will show a sac with no baby inside and can be a real shock to discover.

A **Molar Pregnancy** is where an abnormal fertilised egg implants in the womb. The cells which should be the placenta, grow rapidly and there's no space for the embryo to grow and develop.

An **Ectopic Pregnancy** is where the egg fertilises in a place other than the womb and most commonly in the fallopian tube.

Recurrent Miscarriage – is when there are three or more miscarriages in a row. The egg fertilises and but doesn't grow and usually happens early in the trimester. It is recurrent because it happens consecutively and often when the woman is trying to get pregnant through IVF.

Late Miscarriage is where the baby dies between the 14 - 20 week mark. It is also called second-trimester or mid-trimester miscarriage as it happens in the middle stage of pregnancy, according to the medical profession in the UK. It is hard to understand, when you lose your baby between 20 and 23 weeks and 6 days, why it is called a Miscarriage, especially as there is no birth or death certificate. This is because the viability of a baby in the UK is 24 weeks. This was my experience and there is nothing worse than giving birth to your much wanted baby who a) has died in the womb or b) the baby you know isn't going to survive after birth or c) the baby which dies during birth.

Stillbirth – is the death of a baby after 24 weeks either before or during birth and mostly the baby has to be birthed. If your baby is born after 24 weeks you are entitled to a birth and death certificate in the UK.

* Resource https://www.miscarriageassociation.org.uk

Whether you've had a missed miscarriage, blighted ovum, a late miscarriage, stillbirth, recurrent miscarriage, molar pregnancy or ectopic pregnancy, the pain of loss can be heavy to bear.

From the moment you know you're pregnant you will tend to love and feel connected to your baby. I say mostly because sometimes you don't want to be pregnant, maybe it's the wrong time, you're not ready or you really didn't want to have children.

As soon as you become pregnant your dreams of having a child escalate, you're already imagining how you're going to decorate the nursery, if it's a boy or girl, what school they'll attend, what they'll do with their life, and what they will become. It all happens in our vision and the love mostly forms instantly for the being you're carrying. It is a part of you, so close, so unseen, yet always there and growing little by little each day until for some reason it stops growing.

The horror you feel when you go to the scan and see there isn't a heartbeat, or when you find you're bleeding or when you're halfway through your pregnancy and discover an anomaly. Nothing can describe those feelings of loss; it just feels like the bottom has fallen out of your world. It's a pain that you'd never believe you could feel, so deep, so dark, so traumatic. I remember the pain, the disbelief, and the shock of not knowing what was happening or how things would turn out before I 'birthed' my baby. There was an underlying feeling of hope that things would turn out to be ok, that the medical profession had got it wrong. I didn't know what to do. I was at home, scared and alone. I felt numb, not wanting to communicate with anyone. I felt like a shell, like a robot just going through the motions.

Different Emotions You Might Face and Feel

There is a myriad of different emotions you might feel when you find out that you are no longer carrying your child. You may feel a lot of different emotions or you may feel one overriding emotion, such as sadness. Sadness is the most heart-wrenching of emotions and most of us feel this as the overwhelming emotion. I remember feeling sad all the time, it felt like a cloak around me — heavy, permeating and weighing me down. As it's all part of the grief cycle, we have to feel it, face it, embrace it and bit by bit it becomes less as life goes on. However, you may find (and it's normal) that it will always be a part of you, just not as intense.

- **Sadness** is an emotional pain associated with feelings of disadvantage, loss, despair, grief, helplessness, disappointment and sorrow. Sadness is a natural part of life and may manifest physically in tears or a crushing pain in the chest.

- **Grief** is associated with loss. It's a cycle we go through after a life-changing event, mostly death. We can also feel grief after a relationship break-up, being made redundant from a job we loved, and it usually comes when something we love is taken away. I talk more about the grief cycle in the next section.

- **Anger** is a secondary emotion because we tend to resort to anger in order to protect ourselves from, or to cover up, vulnerable feelings. We mostly always feel something else first before we get angry. Most anger is generally short-lived. No one is born with a long-term anger problem. It's a learned response. In this situation, you may feel angry towards your doctor, the medical staff, your partner, your friends or at life in general.

   Anger is part of the grief cycle and it's very common to feel angry about what has happened to you. I remember feeling angry, thinking, 'Why has this happened to me?' and 'What have I done to deserve this?' It's best to feel it and release it, as anger can eat you up inside.

- **Relief** is a reaction to the sudden freedom from a strong fear or anticipation of something.

  It may sound a little odd to feel relief after losing your baby. However, to some it is pertinent. I've had women tell me that they felt relief after the miscarriage as they were worried about having a baby for financial reasons, or they thought they weren't ready to bring a baby into the world, or they were a single-parent and worried about how they'd manage to do it alone. Sometimes their relationship isn't strong enough to add a baby to the mix. Tinged with sadness often there is relief. It is normal to feel it at times, so don't be hard on yourself. It's part of the balance of emotions.

- **Jealousy** is thoughts or feelings of insecurity, fear, concern and envy due to a desire for something of personal value. It's very common to feel jealousy and envy after something we greatly desire has been taken away and others have what we desperately want.

  Jealousy is something that comes up time and time again with the women I talk to. It is the over-riding complication they face when they see women with a newborn or hear their friend or close family member is pregnant. It is something that brings up rawness and hurt, and is also something they are ashamed of feeling. If this is you, acknowledge it and all it brings up, work through it and try not to let it 'own' or define you. It's okay to feel like this, it's a normal reaction but it becomes unhealthy when it takes over your life. Be aware of how much you begin to obsess about it and when you find it controlling you, seek professional help. It feels much better when you can offload this feeling to another person who you can trust. I remember it literally took my breath away when I saw a pregnant woman. Just know that this too shall pass.

- **Depression** is a state of low mood and aversion to activity that can affect a person's thoughts, behaviour, feelings and sense of wellbeing. It is a normal temporary reaction to life events, such as the loss of a loved one. You may be feeling depressed for some days or weeks after your loss. If it is ongoing please seek help.

We can fall into a depressed state when we have lost something or someone very dear to us and I know I did. I had a low mood for several months intermittently and remember my doctor telling me she thought I was depressed! That woke me up. I didn't want to be depressed and go on antidepressants, so I decided to pay attention to my moods. I found that gentle exercise helped, walks and talks with friends and long soaks in a bath with some uplifting essential oils, such as lavender, sweet orange oil, bergamot oil (be careful not to be in the sunlight after using bergamot as it is photosensitive, and you may burn in the sun. However, it is safe to use in a diffuser or burner). Low vitamin D is linked to depression and I would urge you to have your levels assessed. I went to a nutritionist as the method they use is more accurate. Sunshine activates vitamin D, so a holiday in the sun would definitely help. There's nothing like a change of scene to alter your mood. Reiki healing also helped me get through this phase.

- **Blame** can be felt after a loss when feelings of sadness, hurt, and probably anger occur, and we look to someone to be accountable. This can be levelled at your partner, the medical sector or ourselves—self-blame is common after a miscarriage. Please know that there is very little you could have done to stop your miscarriage; for some reason, your baby just wasn't forming correctly and this, in all likelihood, was nothing to do with you or what you did and didn't do.

  Blame is a common emotion felt after losing your baby. When we are angry it's very easy to point the finger of blame. It's a destructive and pointless emotion and no one wins here, least of all you. Carrying blame in our energy weighs heavy on us, especially if the blame is directed inwards. After my loss, I had a post-mortem because I desperately wanted to know the cause and I felt that would help me understand and move on. It did. The report came back with CMV (Cytomegalovirus) an airborne virus anyone can catch at any time and is hosted within the human body. This can affect you during pregnancy, which sadly was my reality. My partner, on the other hand, blamed the medical profession for the amniocentesis they performed. I couldn't bear to go along with this as it cast too many aspersions; we were aware of the risks, as it was an invasive technique. Whether it was the fault of the amniocentesis, I will never know and at this stage in my life, it really doesn't matter. It has happened, I have dealt with it and it serves me no purpose in pursuing this further.

- **Shame** is a painful feeling that is a mix of regret, self-hate and dishonour. A good person would feel shame if they cheated on a test or said something unkind to a friend or family member. Feeling shame is one of the most miserable feelings of them all and is something that can often be felt after a miscarriage. You might feel shame that you weren't able to carry a baby; this primal instinct that seems to be our God-given right as a female. You might be feeling like your body has let you down. It can be a normal part of your grieving cycle to feel this, but please don't let it become a big part. Look at the bigger picture and a good exercise for this is the 'Coffee Table' exercise. Imagine there is a coffee table; put all your thoughts and feelings on the table. Everything you think, feel and believe about your miscarriage, take them out of your head and put them on the coffee table. See them there, sitting away from you and picture yourself sitting on a chair away from the coffee table. Once you've separated yourself from these thoughts, feelings and beliefs you can see them objectively. Look at them from outside of yourself—they are just items sitting on a coffee table and are no longer part of you. Let them stay on the coffee table because they no longer serve you.

Shame was an emotion I didn't feel acutely. I probably felt more unease in certain situations, for example, when I had to explain to someone I wasn't pregnant anymore and deal with those uncomfortable situations. It's uncomfortable because the person you're speaking to then feels bad for asking and you feel uncomfortable having to repeat the conversation time and time again. I began to wish I had a flash-card I could hand over answering all the questions. Yes, I was pregnant. Sadly, I am no longer. We had a late pregnancy loss; this is what happened. Then you have to listen to all the platitudes, for example, "At least you know you can get pregnant"—my most disliked of them all. Not helpful! Yes, I can get pregnant, but I wanted to carry *this* baby to full-term!

Do know that whatever emotion you are feeling, at one time, you'll also be feeling another emotion subconsciously. Life is not black and white – it is tinged with grey. Sometimes we feel sad, sometimes we feel happy, sometimes we feel guilty, sometimes we don't, sometimes we feel blame, sometimes we feel thankful, sometimes we feel jealous or envious and other times we feel unresentful. At no given time of the day do we feel one emotion, there is always a balance of them. Some good, some not so good, it's what makes us human.

In the next chapter, I will be sharing further strategies on how you can support and heal yourself from all the above negative emotions.

Understanding The Wheel of Grief

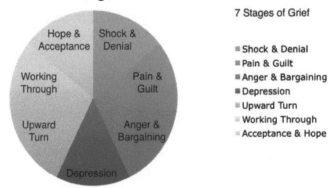

7 Stages of Grief

- Shock & Denial
- Pain & Guilt
- Anger & Bargaining
- Depression
- Upward Turn
- Working Through
- Acceptance & Hope

We all go through a grief cycle after a loss and it's helpful to know and identify where you are in the cycle. It can take anything from one to two years, or more, to complete the cycle fully. This is where you can learn to be kind to yourself and not expect too much of yourself. I remember thinking that I *should* feel better by now. It's a very personal journey and some of us will take longer than others to complete the cycle. Now that you are aware of this, just go with it and note the different cycles.

- **Shock and Denial**. You get the bad news and you go into denial that it is happening - surely, it's a mistake? "This can't be happening to me", you might say. You can feel light-headed, nauseous and physically weak or numb and mechanical during this stage.

19

- **Pain and Guilt**. We start to feel the pain. The shock has left and the pain comes in usually accompanied by guilt. "What did I do wrong?" is generally the first question we ask ourselves. We feel guilty for having had a glass of wine or eating unhealthy foods or not taking our pregnancy supplements, etc. The guilt we ladle on ourselves can be insurmountable and is certainly not helpful. Guilt is a useless emotion and just sucks our energy and brings us down. You'd never say to someone you love what you say to yourself, so start giving yourself some compassion. This is NOT your fault, it has, in all likelihood, happened for biological reasons. The cells haven't formed properly and the body has rejected them.

- **Anger and Bargaining**. Anger can be directed at yourself, a loved one or God and the universe. When this happens, it is generally misplaced. Then comes bargaining; we think, "If I hadn't done x then this wouldn't have happened" or "If only I had done something different, it may not have happened." We start to bargain with ourselves and we can also be unconsciously angry at the baby for dying. Again, this is a huge energy drain and can lead to depression.

- **Depression.** We spiral down to feeling depressed and low. We can't be bothered to do anything. We feel physically and mentally lethargic and our mood is low.

- **Upward Turn**. We start to come out of the low mood and apathy. We see light at the end of the tunnel.
- **Working Through**. We start to work it through in our minds. We reconcile with our thoughts and emotions.
- **Acceptance and Hope**. We are in the final stage here. We start to accept what has happened and begin to look to the future and find hope: hope that we can try again, hope that life will get better and hope that the future looks brighter.

The cycle of grief is different for everyone and you may take longer to come out of a particular stage. You may also find you slip back in and out of a particular stage as well. Don't get too worried if this happens, each person is different, and it can be helpful to know which stage you find yourself in the cycle.

Interestingly, while writing this book, my father died and so I have been going through the grief cycle myself. In the beginning, when told, I was in shock—my body shut down, I felt dizzy, nauseous and weak. I was unable to tap into my emotions. I felt I was on auto-pilot and just going through the motions for about 12 hours. Then someone sent me a heartfelt message, and that set me off, I was able to then cry and start to release my grief. A lot of the time I felt I wanted to be alone because being with people was too tiring and then I began to want to open up and talk to people. Grief hits in waves; sometimes you're feeling perfectly fine, and then you'll have a memory, a thought or hear music that will set you off crying again. It's interesting how somehow when it matters, you can dig deep and find the strength to go on.

I was giving a eulogy for my father and the morning of the funeral I was consumed with grief, not knowing if I could pull myself together to read the eulogy. After my initial meltdown, I took myself away for some quiet time. I used my Rescue Remedy and did some deep breathing using a yoga strategy called lion's breath where you exhale everything out in a forceful way. I also used EAM (The Energy Alignment Method) where I released the stuck energy I was feeling in my chest and heart and, once released, I brought in some powerful, positive affirmations, such as, "I am calm, relaxed, confident and empowered. I allow this into my energy, in all forms, on all levels, at all points in time!" I repeated this many times until I felt it settle into my energy and from there I was able to read the eulogy (which was 10 minutes long) and felt I did my father proud.

During this time, I discovered that this grief – the grief of losing a loved one – and the grief of losing a baby were different. It was somehow a different outer and inner experience. The grief of losing a baby was more intense because it's part of you that is lost; an intimate part of yourself has gone, something within you so deep, so personal and so raw.

At the time, I posted in my miscarriage and pregnancy loss support group and shared how I felt it was a different type of grief I was feeling and many knew exactly where I was coming from. Those that had lost loved ones (family and close friends) and had also lost a baby felt it was a different type of grief.

You may have experienced both and have your own comparisons – both are crippling and this is not to take one away from the other – just an interesting observation. The grief of losing your baby during pregnancy is intangible. It is an unfamiliar experience to the rest of the world; they haven't a notion what you're feeling and going through. They're not the one who has encountered it and so they can't relate to what you are going through. This is to give you an understanding of why people often come across as flippant about your loss. The following is an article I wrote for www.psychologies.co.uk which may be useful to you and I'm sure you can relate. I'd love for you to share it with your friends and family if you're going through a loss at the time of reading this book. It just might help them to help you.

What to Say to Your Friend or Family Member After a Miscarriage or Pregnancy Loss

As Baby Loss Awareness Week approaches (9-15th October) it's good to be mindful of your friend or family member's loss.

I lost two pregnancies and know how difficult it is to heal. As a result, I now mentor hundreds of clients through miscarriage and pregnancy loss. I know how little support I had after the event and wasn't surprised when I carried out a survey and discovered that 95% of women had no support or counselling. They said that one of the biggest issues was that their friends or family members weren't there for them in the way they wanted them to be, or their partners didn't know what to say or do.

I've put together a list of 'dos and don'ts' to help you or someone you know who is going through this:

What NOT to say:

- "At least you know you can get pregnant." This is probably one of the worst things you can say as it is of very little comfort when you can get pregnant but are not able to carry your baby to full-term.

- "You can try again." Replacing your lost, dearly wanted baby quickly isn't the answer as she wanted THIS baby.

- "It wasn't meant to be." This is of little comfort as the mother is acutely aware something went wrong but can only see in hindsight that it wasn't meant to be. At the time, all she can think about is why did this happen and why wasn't this meant to be, why me?

- "Better luck next time." This trivialises her loss and is incredibly insensitive; the sort of thing an awkward uncle may blurt out!

- However, the worst thing you can say is nothing at all and pretending it hasn't happened because you don't know what to say.

DO say:

- "I'm so sorry for your loss." She will feel valued and understood.

- "I'm here for you... Please tell me how you are." Sometimes she needs a shoulder to cry on and someone to talk to about it. Sometimes she needs to silently cry in her own space. Remember to keep in contact with her; a daily text or phone call helps her realise it's not such a lonely place to be.

- If you can't visit or feel uncomfortable about it (especially if you're pregnant or just had a baby) send her some flowers, chocolates or a meal. The last thing she'll be thinking of is cooking. I was so grateful when a friend turned up on my doorstep with a home-cooked dinner.

- Do ask what they need. Everyone is different. They may want to go out for a girly night, or stay in and watch a film. They may just want to have you be there with them. Sometimes she might just want to be alone to grieve in her own way.

In my experience, women who have lost babies need to talk about it, to be heard and have their loss acknowledged. Encourage them to talk to you. Also, do be aware of anniversaries of the time it happened and her due dates because she won't ever forget.

Healing from this is a long process and eventually, she will be ready to 'try again'. She will never forget you being there for her. Equally, she will never forget if you weren't there for her. Remember, it's the small things that count.

Will I Ever Feel Normal Again?

This was the overriding feeling I had after my loss: Will I ever feel normal again? I used to wake up in the morning and for the first split second everything was 'normal' then the realisation hit me like a tonne of bricks. I couldn't imagine what it was like to feel back to my normal self and it was something I aspired to.

In time, I realised that I would never be the same as I was and had to adapt to a 'new normal'. After grief, there is always a period of adjustment to find your 'new normal' and once you find it, you can settle into it. Don't be afraid to let go of the angst and the energy of your loss because this can keep you in the same state of heaviness. It's okay to let it go because once you let it go, something amazing will come into your life. Imagine you have your arms full of stuff, so full that nothing else can fit in. When you let one of those things go then something new can fit in. It's a case of letting go of the old stuff that no longer serves you and let in some goodies, which make you feel better. You deserve to feel better; everyone does. Sometimes people think, "If I let go of the pain, I'll be letting go of my beloved baby I so dearly wanted," so they hold onto those emotions. By holding onto them you're no closer to having the baby you desire. It's not about forgetting the baby you carried and loved, you'll never forget them. They will always be a part of you and by feeling and releasing the emotion you can start to heal.

Conclusion

The feelings and emotions we can experience are varied and not all of them will apply personally to you. By listing and explaining them, you can see which category you fall into and then deal with them accordingly. You may experience different emotions at different times and again, this is completely normal. It's important to acknowledge how you are feeling so you can identify and objectively say to yourself, "I'm feeling like this today and that's okay, this too shall pass." It will pass. Remember you have to go through it all until you come out the other side; it's a process and time is a great healer. It takes time to feel less raw, it takes time to come to a feeling of acceptance and it takes time to start to feel your 'new normal' again. Remember that it is okay to feel these emotions, as painful as they are they are part of the healing cycle. Shutting yourself down, feeling numb and disconnecting from life will mean that you are simply going through life on autopilot.

Disconnection is something humans often do to protect themselves from feeling and it's a coping strategy. I would urge you to feel the pain and let it pass, be aware of what you're feeling and this will enable you to heal much quicker. You may be thinking that you can't bear to feel the pain and therefore want to numb yourself to it, which is keeping you safe. Let the lid come off and often times you'll be surprised how cathartic it is to get messy; to scream and howl and beat the bed and be primal. The pain is primal. It is intense and rocks the core of you, but there's only one way to go after you've got to this point and that's up. You'll feel relief, an inner calm and somehow sated. It will be worth it when you come out the other side.

It is important for you and us as humans to be connected to our emotions, to feel our emotions, to be aware of what is going on, to pay attention to what is going on within us and then we can do something about it. We can change our state, we can become less stuck and we can ultimately feel better.

Emotions are felt on a physiological, psychological and an energetic level. Everyone 'feels' these differently and that is down to our DNA and experiences. For example, a person working in a field of high-pressure or stress, like the armed forces, the police or the fire-brigade, etc will have a more enhanced stress response due to the nature of their work. As such, they may experience and be affected by negative emotions in a stronger way, or conversely may have them locked up so they can carry on.

Ultimately, humans are programmed to be happy. We weren't born feeling unhappy; we became unhappy when basic needs weren't met when we were hungry, tired or in pain. Once those needs were met, we were happy again. However, society teaches us to button up, to get on with it, to not make a fuss and to endure our emotional, mental and physical pain in silence. This can, in turn, create depression and mental health problems. If we would only feel free to speak about the difficulties we are going through there would be less mental health issues, depression, anxiety and suicides in the world. There is only so much pain a human can take and when the pain becomes too much to bear on one's own, often the only way a person feels they can get out of the situation can mean taking drastic measures.

Candace Pert, author of *Molecules of Emotion* dedicated her life's work in biochemistry to scientifically prove that emotions affect our mind and body. In a nutshell, she discovered the opiate receptor which bonds endorphins and discovered the mind-body connection. In brief, (here comes the science bit) when we feel an emotion these molecules are made up of peptides which are sent to receptors, which send messages to make changes in the cells of our body.

Imagine there is a peptide of anger being sent to the liver and locked there. If it keeps being sent there repetitively it can create changes on a cellular level and an energetic level. The impact of this change is also felt on a hormonal level where receptors in our body have received the hormones.

This is how we manifest disease in our body; the hormone receptors are creating massive changes on a cellular level and so we feel the impact on our body. On a psychological level, our emotions are an input of our brain and mental thought processes. What we think and then experience as emotions is what effects the way we feel.

This is where EAM (The Energy Alignment Method) works so well for me. As an EAM Mentor, I work with the person to help release these 'stuck' emotions, as emotion is 'energy in motion' and can, with the right guidance, pass through and be released from our physical body. It moves through the seven layers of our energy body, the etheric, the emotional, the mental, the astral, the celestial and the divine layers (also known as our aura). It is incredibly beautiful to witness and facilitate this release. The person leaves feeling like a weight has been lifted from their shoulders. They feel lighter, happier, full of hope for the future and with a feeling that anything is possible.

We can change our emotional set points from those we regularly revert back to because it's what our subconscious mind knows from past experience. It happens in our brain because the brain is used to firing this way (our default pattern) to a new emotional set point which can become our new default pattern. We can become addicted to these negative emotions, they are as addictive as a drug;

the more we think that way, the more we want to think that way. It becomes our drug and it becomes our story. We write about it on social media and will tell anyone who'll listen. If you know about the Law of Attraction, the more energy you put into something, thinking about it, writing about it and speaking about it then the more you attract the same thing back to you.

Then there is secondary gain: What gain do we have by being stuck in this loop? It may be that we don't have to go out and see people, we don't have to attend family functions, we don't have the energy to cook, to eat properly, we don't want to go back to work or we don't have to exercise—all because we feel lethargic and possibly depressed. This is our secondary gain to being addicted to a negative emotion. Do you recognise any of these? Secondary gain is subconscious; we don't consciously go out to think about what we can do to keep small, or down. It is our subconscious keeping us safe.

The good news is that we can retrain what is in our energy so that the brain and heart are creating a new set point of something we choose to experience. It's incredibly powerful and exciting to know that there is a new way to deal with our emotional, mental, physical and energetic pain. That we don't have to be in a downward spiral of negativity and that all it takes is an awareness that there is something better out there, that there is help and that there is light at the end of the tunnel. We can make shifts, we can feel better and we can aspire to be happy again; we can feel love, joy and freedom. Love, joy and freedom are at the top of the energetic emotional scale. When we feel these emotions, our energy frequency is transmitting at the highest and fastest pace. We are 'in flow'. Things are going well. Life is great! This is where we want to be. The more of this we feel, the more we attract, as per the Law of Attraction. Conversely when we are feeling low, depressed and fearful our energy frequency is transmitting at a slow, dull pace and life becomes a struggle then we attract more of the same.

If you are holding onto your emotions, not feeling them or letting them go after some time your body will begin to show signs of disease. You may get a skin disorder, become ill with flu, get repetitive colds, become extremely tired and depressed or suffer from insomnia. In some cases, more serious diseases may manifest. It is more than worth it to feel the pain, go through it and come out the other side with a body at-ease, healthy and able to cope.

"Everything in excess is opposed by nature."
— *Hippocrates*

Chapter 2: Embrace Your Healing Journey

Some of the things we do to cope with adversity aren't always the best for us, but we do them anyway because we don't know what else to do. We want to get through the pain in any way we can. I've included some of the less healthy and most common ones here to alert you to what you may be doing that isn't actually helping you. We are going to look at these because I want you to get better in a healthier way with less stress on you and your body.

Coping mechanisms are a form of self-medicating and the reason you're doing it is because you've lost your baby and are feeling awful, so you apply some of these to start to feel better. We usually use them when we are feeling sad, lonely, bored, overwhelmed, fearful or lost. I tend to numb my pain by eating chocolate—it has always been my 'go-to' in times of trouble, boredom or stress. These coping strategies seem to be automatic responses and this compounds the negative impacts on your health.

We are going to explore more about these and I will list some of the most common coping mechanisms people adopt. Some may resonate with you more than others and you'll know which is your go-to, favourite one. I clearly remember, when I was introduced, by a school friend, to eating an entire packet of chocolate marshmallow teacakes (Mallow Puffs) in one go. It hadn't occurred to me to eat for comfort and she explained that this was what she did when she was sad, or upset. This was not a good habit to be introduced to and something I have struggled with for many years to overcome, however, we can change them if we decide to. Remember that they become habits; something we have most likely formed in our past, something that gives us comfort and something we can change when we begin to notice our default patterns.

Coping Mechanisms

Consuming caffeine. Most of us enjoy a daily caffeine intake whether that is coffee or tea. The occasional coffee isn't going to do you much harm, but it is important to remember that caffeine is a drug and it's possible to have a full-blown caffeine addiction. More likely and common is caffeine dependence where people use caffeine to jump-start their energy in the morning, use it throughout the day to stave off a 'caffeine crash' and then find their sleep is disturbed, causing them to wake up tired and need the caffeine jolt to get going again. The cycle continues and caffeine affects stress levels. It's really important to get enough sleep during this time, as it's when the mind finally switches off that you are given some reprieve from what is happening in the world. Try to lessen your caffeine intake because you don't want it interfering with your sleep. Sleep is paramount in healing and you need to have as much as possible. When you sleep your brain switches off and gives your body, mind and soul time to heal. The old adage that you'll feel better in the morning is because you've been able to switch off and coffee or caffeine stops that happening.

Smoking. For smokers, a cigarette can feel like a good stress reliever. During times of stress, a cigarette feels almost necessary and quitting the habit can seem virtually impossible. It's a physical addiction and partly a social and lifestyle habit. Smoking creates much more stress than it alleviates—it's more than worth it to kick the habit. People tend to reach for a cigarette when they want to feel better. Unfortunately, that relief is temporary and inhaling smoke into your lungs isn't good for your breathing. The nicotine in the tobacco is addictive and our bodies crave more—the more we have, the more we want. We are reaching out for help, but this help isn't doing us any good. What is good about smoking is the inhaling of a deep breath and exhaling out. However, it stops right there. Do some deep breathing with clean oxygen and exhale the CO_2 when feeling stressed or anxious.

Drinking in excess. Many of us find that a glass of wine can be a good way to unwind at the end of a stressful day. Drinking can be a slippery slope as excessive drinking can cause problems in virtually every area of a person's life, causing much more stress in the long run. I'm sure I don't need to tell you what excessive drinking does to your liver and how it affects your sleep patterns, but I will just ask you to check in with yourself about how much you are numbing your pain by drinking? Alcohol is a depressant, although often people use it to temporarily feel better and mask pain. We talk about the 'The Wheel of Grief' on Page 18 which includes depression. Excessive drinking may prolong and disrupt the natural grief response and you may stay in the depression cycle longer. There is a wonderful organisation in the UK called Club Soda. If you are concerned about your intake, check out their website: www.joinclubsoda.co.uk. If you are someone who has trouble limiting alcohol consumption to one or two drinks and find that you are drinking more than usual to block out the pain, it would be in your best interests to look at other forms of stress relief such as those mentioned in Chapter three and, in addition to those, exercise.

Compulsive spending. While buying yourself a nice gift once in a while can be a nice pick-me-up and an effective self-care strategy, compulsively buying things to relieve stress or feel good about yourself and spending money you don't have on things you don't really need can cause more financial stress and, in the long run, can contribute to feelings of shame. It's very easy with the internet to order in gifts, clothes or something for the home at a click of a button, but take a moment and ask yourself if you really need it. You really don't want to put yourself under financial stress.

Emotional eating. This is my 'go-to' and sometimes I think I was eating my grief. Some of us reach for chocolate, ice-cream, chips (crisps) or biscuits to help us through and if this is your main coping mechanism for stress, sadness and loss, it can lead to compromised health, excessive weight gain and then feelings of guilt and shame can come into play. When you feel the need to reach for a chocolate bar, take a moment and breathe deeply or go and have a glass of water. Most of the time when we think we are hungry we are simply thirsty. We can often eat when we are bored and finding something interesting to do will help. My mother said "keep your hands busy" and in those days she would knit, make something, do patchwork or embroidery. It's a good strategy and if you can find something to do it will help.

Taking drugs. Again another way to escape, and this is probably the deepest form of escapism, where we retreat into a psychoactive state. Life is happening, but we are totally removed from it. It's like we are watching what is happening from another planet, removed, distant and disconnected from what we are feeling inside. A blissful state for many, but coming down and being back in reality is difficult to deal with, so you can't wait to get the next hit to get high again. It becomes all-encompassing and can totally take over your life, leaving your mental, physical and emotional health in a state of flux. Of course, people take drugs in different ways and can keep it from becoming addictive, only having the occasional hit. If you have an addictive personality, it's better to keep away from trying drugs.

Exercise. Exercise can be a great way of reducing apathy and feeling and increasing your emotional well-being and it can also be addictive. It produces a natural high of serotonin, which is great for making you feel better. It's when you become addicted to it that it can be counterproductive as it can take over your life and also leave your body becoming overused and prone to injury. A lot of people I know are 'running' away from their problems – or trying to 'out-run' them – and I can understand why you'd want to. Keeping a balance between healthy exercise and 'running' away from your problems is key. Sometimes, in this case, your body is telling you to slow down – watch for the signs – you can easily become injured, pull a muscle or get bursitis in the joints, in which case you have no choice but to stop. It's a great distraction from stressful situations as well as a good outlet for your frustrations and gives you a lift from the endorphins released as you exercise. Whether you choose to go running, walking, cycling, the gym, or play a contact sport, exercise will certainly provide great relief. Do make sure you are physically ready before hitting the gym or taking up a new exercise regime and build it up slowly. I remember when

I returned from the hospital, I decided to clean the kitchen floor on my hands and knees (even though I had a mop) because I wanted to have a physical outlet and do something that appeared normal. It was a foolish idea and illustrates how we can behave in times of angst and engage in activities which are out of character to lessen our pain. I really wasn't feeling fit or well enough and it set me back so much so that I was readmitted to the hospital for a week as I had sepsis and was put on an antibiotic drip. I had nothing else to do but face my pain as I was confined to the hospital bed.

Busyness. This is when we are keeping ourselves busy, so we don't stop, feel or think about what is really going on—not being present. It's not a good idea to wait until you're on the edge of a breakdown to address something that is hurting you. When you are too busy sometimes that's the only way to get your attention. Be aware of not keeping yourself too busy, shutting out the pain and numbing yourself. In *Daring Greatly* Brené Brown writes about numbing behaviours that we use as armour against vulnerability. She writes, 'We are a culture of people who've bought into the idea that if we stay busy enough, the truth of our lives won't catch up with us.'

Box set bingeing. We all like a box set to have some downtime in our busy world. It often helps us to shut off from and decompress after a busy day or week. Again, it's another coping strategy which (although it is fun and who doesn't love a new box set to get our teeth into) can become addictive and all-consuming. A recent study published in the Journal of Clinical Sleep Medicine found that binge-watching could be bad for us. It was reported that binge-watching caused more fatigue, insomnia symptoms, poorer sleep quality and feeling more alert before going to sleep. Those who binge-watched had 98% more chance of having poor quality sleep than those that didn't. According to Robert Oexman, director of the 'Sleep to Live Institute', looking at bright screens, especially at night, can wreak havoc on your biology because it is one of the cues that helps maintain our circadian rhythm or body clock. When it gets dark our bodies start to prepare for sleep, but bright lights can trick our brains into thinking it's still daytime. He says if you're going to do it, try to do it before 6 p.m. and restrict it to weekends instead of weeknights. Try and turn your screen off one hour before getting ready for bed.

Procrastination. Procrastination is more than simply spending time on Facebook before starting work. At a foundational and psychological level, putting off your responsibilities for what seems like innocent short-term pleasure is a powerful emotional coping mechanism, says Dr Tim Pychyl, Professor of Psychology at Carleton University in Ottawa, Canada. He recommends breaking tasks down into smaller parts and then beginning to work on one or two of those parts a little earlier than you normally would. Beating procrastination also requires intention, so formulate 'if/then' statements in your mind like, "If the phone rings, then I'm not going to answer." This is good if you are putting off doing what you know you must do, whether that is at home or at work or socially. You know at some point you are going to have to speak to someone you'd really rather not talk to about your loss: the neighbour, an acquaintance or someone you bump into on the street.

Conclusion

Coping mechanisms are wide and varied and we all have our favourites. You are not wrong for having them; they are simply a way for you to cope with the pain until your true healing begins. You might want to think about how many you are using and if they are serving you in your life. Ask if the coping mechanism is getting you closer to where you want to go and how you want to feel, or further away? Think about ways in which you can do less of them and focus on the outcome of what you really want to bring into your life, what you desire and how you'd love your life to be.

"Start by doing what's necessary; then do what's possible, and suddenly you are doing the impossible."

— *Francis of Assisi*

Chapter 3: Supporting Self/ Self-Healing

It's very easy after you've had a loss to try to numb yourself to the pain. After all, there is a gaping hole in your life and you want to fill it with something to make yourself feel better. Often, we try to numb ourselves so we don't feel the pain. This can take many forms, for example, eating lots of sugary and unhealthy foods, drinking alcohol, binge-watching TV or Netflix and taking drugs—anything to numb the pain.

It's very important not to numb the pain because, firstly, you're creating more stress on your body and mind. If you're eating the wrong foods you'll be putting on weight, if you're drinking too much, it will be impacting your liver function. Our liver is where all the toxins in the body are processed and when it's not working optimally you'll be storing them in your body, which can lead to health problems such as extra weight, an excess of hormones to name a few.

What can happen when you numb yourself is that you're shutting down mentally and physically—it's a form of storing up the pain and sweeping it under the carpet.

It will come up later as what goes in has to come out at some point. This will either manifest physically by getting physically ill or will result in anxiety or depression. At some point, it will bubble up to the surface and smack you hard in the face when you're least expecting it.

So, what can you do instead of numbing your pain? Over the past twenty years, I've trained and worked in several holistic therapies, including aromatherapy, (the use of essential oils) hypnotherapy and Reiki, as well as, mindfulness and visualisation techniques and most recently trained as an Energy Alignment Method Mentor (EAM). I'd like to share my top tips with you so you can start to implement them and begin your healing process.

1) The Energy Alignment Method (EAM)

The Energy Alignment Method is an award-winning self-help technique, designed by Yvette Taylor, to help you shift anything that is going on in your head and your heart. It enables you to let go of resistant energy, limiting beliefs and negative emotions, so you can replace them with positive thoughts and emotions and feel more in flow. If you're a fan of things like the Law of Attraction, mindfulness, NLP (Neuro-linguistic programming) EFT (Emotional Freedom Technique) or CBT (Cognitive Behavioural

Therapy) you'll love EAM. It's a quick way of changing your energy. EAM is a transformational self-help method based on a foundation of energy medicine, neuroscience research, the Law of Attraction and traditional Chinese medicine. This powerful five-step technique combines principles from kinesiology, neuro-linguistic programming and positive psychology to enable you to feel happy and empowered to change your life. With EAM you will know how to transform your energy, change what you think and shift how you feel instantly. I'm one of the first mentors trained in this modality and I've found it to be the quickest way to release stress and stuck emotions, limiting beliefs and patterns (resistance). There are five steps to EAM and we use the body as a pendulum to get a yes or no answer (a kinesiology technique) which is an ideomotor response from your energy.

Step 1 – You ask – This step is to give you clarity on what you need to shift. Ask your energy a simple question, about a subject to see if it is something you need to work on. For example, "Am I holding any resistance or worry when I think about my miscarriage?"

Step 2 You Move – Your energy body will respond and give you the YES or NO answer to the question you asked. Forward is usually YES and usually being NO. If it sways another way it could be an Energy Reversal.

Step 3 – You Experience – This step is all about assessing what is happening in your energy when you think about that subject. For now, let's look at three ways for you to do this step. Choose which is appropriate for you:

1) What happens to your energy? Describe the size/colour/shape/location/etc.

2) How many of something do you have? Use the sway to identify the number.

3) Which emotions do you feel? Use the emotional scale to see.

4) Explore clarifying questions. Ask further questions to get more details.

5) What do you see in your mind's eye? Describe the visual picture.

Step 4 – You Transform – "I am ready to release (whatever you feel). I release it from my energy in all forms, on all levels and at all points in time." Repeat this statement at least three times or until you can no longer feel it.

For example: "I am ready to release this heavy, dark cloud in my stomach/heart (or wherever you feel it) around the loss of my baby – I release it from my energy in all forms, on all levels at all points in time." Repeat three times or until you can no longer feel it.

Step 5 – You Manifest – Say, "I'm ready to allow/ receive/ experience, think, feel (whatever you want to allow in). I allow this into my energy, in all forms, on all levels at all points in time." Repeat this statement three times or more until you can feel it and you have a sway forwards.

For example: "I'm ready to allow and receive peace, love, joy and freedom. I allow this into my energy in all forms, on all levels at all points in time."

This technique will help you because it will change the way you are feeling instantly and get you into a better place emotionally. You'll feel lighter, more relaxed and ready to face the world. This is a basic overview of EAM and there is plenty more to know, but I wanted to give you a synopsis and introduce you to this amazing technique. More details can be found on the website **www.energyalignmentmethod.com** or in Yvette Taylor's book *The Ultimate Self Help Book*.

I have included the emotional energy scale, so you can work through releasing the negative emotions and allowing in the positive emotions by following the structure above.

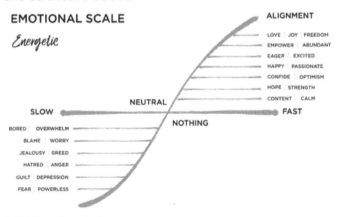

EAM Freedom Ltd ©

2) Aromatherapy Essential Oils

I've used and studied in many different therapies since I first started on my healing journey in 1997. My very first training was at the Tisserand Institute where I completed a diploma in Holistic Aromatherapy and Massage. The study of essential oils and their properties, which affects the physical, emotional, psychological and energetic levels, is fascinating.

There are several ways in which the oils can be administered and the most holistic way is through massage. A trained aromatherapist will take a thorough case history with a client when they arrive, learning about their physical, mental and emotional health in detail, and then will prescribe and create a blend of essential oils which best match with how the client is presenting.

The oils are diluted in vegetable base oil, such as sweet almond oil, grape seed oil, de-fractionated coconut oil, or any other vegetable oil you prefer. I tend to find olive oil a little thick and sticky, which means it doesn't absorb well into the skin. Mineral oils, such as baby lotion, tend to sit on top of the skin and don't absorb well and are not as pure as vegetable based oils. Mostly, a blend of three or four essential oils is used (2.5%) into the base oil. If the base oil is 20 ml then 10 drops of essential oils are used. This is because the essential oils are incredibly strong as they're directly taken from the plant and processed mostly through steam distillation. It is safe to have an aromatherapy massage whilst you're pregnant. In this case, we would use a diluted blend of 1% (a maximum of two drops in 20 ml base oil) which is safe in pregnancy.

The benefit of using essential oils in massage takes it to another level. You have the effect of the oils, which are absorbed by the skin and taken into the body to work on the cells on a physical level, and the effect of the smell which works on the psychological level. For example, oils that help with grief are rose and frankincense. A balancing oil to help balance emotions is geranium. For relaxation, my top two oils are lavender and roman chamomile. Roman chamomile is more expensive than lavender, so if you were considering purchasing essential oils for yourself, geranium, frankincense and lavender would be a nice mix. Also, citrus oils like lemon, sweet orange oil, and grapefruit are very uplifting and smell beautiful.

You can also use essential oils in a diffuser (about eight drops in water) and put it in a room where you're resting. If you don't have a diffuser of any type you can use a saucer with water added and place it on top of a radiator (in winter) and this will disperse the oils into the room.

Another way is to bathe with the oils. Drop some lavender and chamomile or frankincense into your bath. Because it's oil and water mix, you could use a dispersant (home remedy for this is cream or full-fat milk). Not much is needed, but it does help the oils disperse into the water.

If you have trouble sleeping, put a drop (only one drop) onto your pillow. Lavender has the opposite effect if used in quantity. A drop will lull your senses and help switch off a busy mind.

Another top tip is if you're going out and are anxious or worried about it, pop a drop of lavender or geranium onto a tissue and carry it with you, taking a deep breath of it when needed. A drop of geranium on a tissue in the car is wonderful when the traffic is causing delays. Geranium is psychologically balancing and a deep inhale of this will instantly calm you as well as make your car smell wonderfully fragrant. I recommend using good quality oils and the Tisserand brand are ethically and sustainably sourced.

3) Spiritual Healing or Reiki

During my training in Aromatherapy, we explored energy healing which became one of my favourite modules. At this point, I was unaware of healing energy and was totally blown away by it. Our tutor ran a workshop and at that workshop, I met a very special healer, Michael Hartzel, who is based in Woodford Bridge, Essex.

It was here I began my healing journey. I joined Michael's healing group and slowly started to come to terms with my loss. Healing and Reiki are both gentle techniques, sometimes using hands on or off the body, that are used for stress reduction and relaxation. They can complement any medical or psychological care. The body has the ability to heal itself and to do so complete relaxation is often beneficial. Long-term imbalances in the body sometimes require multiple sessions in order to facilitate the level of relaxation needed by the body to heal itself. I had healing from Michael regularly and it kept me grounded and relaxed as I gently let go of all the sadness, anxiety, anger, guilt and blame that I carried with me over losing my baby.

Doing this got me to a place of acceptance and hope. Three years after my loss I conceived again. I was a little worried in my next pregnancy and I continued seeing Michael who kept me relaxed and aligned throughout. My rainbow baby, Lilia, was born on the 1st of June 1999 and what a bundle of joy she was. Between aromatherapy oils and healing, she was a very easy baby and still remains so to this day. My second rainbow baby was born three years later. If you have wondered about having a healing or Reiki session please do give it a try. It is wonderfully relaxing and the benefit is that you will start to feel more at peace with your loss and get yourself into a place where you will be ready to try again, should you wish to do so.

4) Feng Shui

Feng Shui, originating from China, uses energy forces to harmonise people to their surrounding environment and it is becoming much more widely used in Western cultures.

Sarah McAllister, *5D Wellbeing – Designing your life and your home for multidimensional health and happiness*, talks about miscarriage and Feng Shui. Sarah's book has been written for those living in the Northern Hemisphere. If you're reading this and reside in the Southern Hemisphere it will be different for you and I'd advise you to contact Sarah on **sarah@fengshuiagency.com** and she can refer you to practitioners she knows in the Southern Hemisphere. Her book suggests:

- Miscarriage – South West. The South West inside a home is the Earth or Mother Trigram which is the most yin or feminine of all and perfectly reflects the anatomical receptivity of the vagina, womb and stomach. The womb is literally impregnated with male sperm to create life and the stomach is filled with food to sustain life.

- I have viewed many properties where people are trying to get pregnant or keep suffering miscarriages, only to find that the South West position in the floor plan is wholly absent and also has spiky plants or craggy boulders in that direction which are unsettling the chi there.

5) Rescue Remedy

Rescue Remedy is an effective all-natural stress and anxiety reliever created from flower essences. It is available to buy over the counter from most pharmacies and has a comparable effect to traditional pharmaceutical drugs without any of the known adverse side effects, including addiction. It is manufactured by Nelsons and Bach and contains five flower essences: rock rose to alleviate terror and panic. Impatiens to mollify irritation and impatience, clematis to combat inattentiveness, star of Bethlehem to ease shock and cherry plum to calm irrational thoughts. It comes in a spray bottle or drop form. You can put a few drops into your water bottle and sip throughout the day and evening. It helps provide better emotional balance and relief from everyday stress. It's something you can keep with you at all times and use as and when you need it and I frequently use it to this day. I find it useful to have in my bag, as often, when meeting a friend or client, they need support and this helps them get into a calm state quickly. It's wonderful to use on flights, before a job interview, funeral, a speaking event or anytime when you are feeling nervous, anxious or stressed.

6) Yoga

The benefits of practising yoga are immense. It helps you breathe and expand your lungs, stretch out your muscles, it increases flexibility and muscle strength. It's also known to help you feel happier. A study found that doing consistent yoga practise improved depression and led to an increase in serotonin levels (the happy hormone) and decreased the levels of cortisol (the stress hormone). It also encourages you to relax, slow your breath and focus on the present. It slows down the mental loops of frustration, regret, anger and fear. Yoga appears to reduce anger by increasing feelings of compassion, interconnection and by calming the nervous system and the mind. It also increases your ability to step back from the drama of your own life, which after having a miscarriage is a welcome retreat.

You may not particularly feel like going to a yoga class straight after your miscarriage but you can do some gentle exercises at home and find restorative yoga clips on YouTube. A good exercise you can try at home is to roll up a towel or rug and put it lengthways on the floor or mat. Lie back on top of it making sure it's running along your spine. Your head should be resting on the floor or mat. Let your arms drop out and your chest open up. Lie there and breathe for a few minutes. Once you get up you'll feel a little more restored. By doing this you are opening up the chest and this is where we store grief and are usually physically caved in. It's a great stretch for releasing grief and depression.

My yoga teacher, Julie Tortora, who trained with The British Wheel of Yoga in 1982, and has been practising Yoga since 1974, says this:

"Difficult experiences, like the unexpected and often harrowing one of miscarriage, can express themselves in the body in a pattern of unconscious physical holding. This may be a way of protecting ourselves from a feared repetition of events in the future and/or a way of controlling our emotional responses and subduing our memories. For profound healing to occur, loosening those holdings in a supportive environment, can enable greater release of emotions and help body and mind to find balance. Yoga practice, with its combination of gentle stretching, freeing the breath and relaxing the body could be used in a number of ways to help with this. After a miscarriage proceed cautiously, in a containing environment and only when you feel ready."

She advocates the following practices to try:

- Gentle stretches round the heart space to free grief and rage.
- Gentle stretching of the hips and pelvis to recover trust in the workings of the reproductive organs.
- Abdominal breathing to promote homeostasis.
- Lion's breath to expel air.
- Alternate nostril breathing to balance the nervous system.
- Deep relaxation with visualisations for releasing the past and embracing new hope for the future.

7) Meditation

The benefits of sitting in meditation are that it quiets the mind and keeps you in the present. Often it isn't easy to switch off, but the key is to keep bringing your attention back to the breath and focus on your breathing. Feel the breath as you breathe in through your nostrils, follow it as it goes down the back of your throat to your lungs and back up and out your nostrils again. Taking just 10 minutes per day to do this initially is a wonderful way to start the day. It stops the loop of anxious repetitive thoughts and gives your mind a well-earned rest.

You'll be glad you switched off and will certainly feel calmer and relaxed after a meditation practice. My yoga teacher, Julie, says the mind is like a puppy; it scampers off in all directions and needs to be brought back to heel. You can do this by focussing again on your breath.

8) Breathing

Breathing is automatic – we do it mostly without thought and intention – it just happens. In my view, breathing is underrated. The effects of taking a deep breath right up into the tops of your lungs and slowly emptying your breath right down to the stomach are immense. When you breathe into the top nodes of your lungs and release it, you are releasing cortisol (a stress hormone) and adrenaline which have been stored in the body.

I have been going to yoga for many years now and my yoga teacher, Julie, has taught me many breathing techniques which in turn, I have shared with my clients. One of these techniques is 'square breathing':

- Breathe in for the count of one;
- Hold in for the count of one;
- Breathe out for the count of one;
- Hold out for the count of one.
- Breathe in for the count of two;
- Hold in for the count of two;
- Breathe out for the count of two;
- Hold out for the count of two.

- Breathe in for the count of three;
- Hold in for the count of three;
- Breathe out for the count of three;
- Hold out for the count of three.
- Breathe in for the count of four;
- Hold in for the count of four;
- Breathe out for the count of four;
- Hold out for the count of four.
- Breathe in for the count of five;
- Hold in for the count of five;
- Breathe out for the count of five;
- Hold out for the count of five.

You can continue up the scale for as long as you feel comfortable bearing in mind most people don't get past seven or eight counts. If you feel yourself getting light-headed, stop and let your breathing come back to normal. This exercise is especially good when you can't drop off to sleep as it concentrates the mind and again helps to switch off:

- Breathe into the three sections of your lungs.
- Lie down comfortably and put your hands on your stomach.
- Take a deep breath and let your stomach distend.
- Release the breath from your stomach and see your hands come down with the breath.
- Move your hands up to the centre of your chest.

- Breathe in, breathe out and see your hands come down with the breath.
- Move your hands to the upper chest (just under your collarbone) breathe in.
- Release the breath and feel your hands descend.
- Move your hands to the mid part of your chest, breathe in and repeat.
- Move your hands to your stomach and feel your hands rise and fall with the breath.
- Continue this three times each for the upper, mid and lower lungs.

This exercise uses all parts of the lungs and is great for deep relaxation and also feels restorative as you have exhaled the excess hormones no longer needed.

If you tend to feel panicky or anxious and get light headed this exercise is helpful.

- Breathe in for the count of three.
- Deep exhale out for the count of six.
- Continue until you start to feel calmer.

By having a long extended out breath you are releasing the excess carbon dioxide (CO_2) which builds up in the body and can cause panic attacks or feelings of anxiety. Doing this will leave you calmer and more relaxed.

9) Visualisations

The power of visualisation and imagination is not to be underestimated. If you go there in the mind, you'll go there in the body as the body follows suit. You know that the mind can conjure up a feeling. Close your eyes for a moment and imagine a lemon, see the vibrant yellow colour, smell the fresh lemon aroma from the skin, imagine you are cutting the lemon in half, see the drops of the juice escape as the knife cuts through. Now imagine you are picking up half of the lemon and tasting it; can you almost taste the tart flavour on your tongue? Are you salivating? What did you feel? So, now you can understand just how powerful the mind and imagination are.

This exercise helps you to see that what we can imagine or visualise when using all of our senses and the effect it has on the physical body. This is good news if your thoughts and emotions are positive but not so good when you're feeling sad, lonely or depressed as your body will react to that too. There have been many excellent books written on this subject and two of my favourites are *You Can Heal Your Life* by Louise Hay and *It's The Thought That Counts* by David R. Hamilton PhD. They illustrate how our thoughts affect our mood and bodies by physical manifestations. This is also studied in META-Health. If you come across a META-Health practitioner they'll ask what is going on physically for you and equate it with a what is happening on an emotional level and what that is related to in your life. Fascinating stuff!

I'd like to give you an example of a visualisation here for relaxation. Make sure you're comfortable and in a quiet place. Do not do this while driving or operating heavy machinery

- Lie down and relax if you can.
- Take a deep breath and exhale, repeat three times.
- Close your eyes and start to relax.
- Feel the relaxation in your face and head and eyes.
- Feel it move down to your shoulders, arms and fingers.
- Feel your whole back relax down either side of your spine.
- Feel your throat, neck and chest area relax.
- Your hips and pelvis are totally relaxed.
- Your legs, your thighs, front and back your knees your shins and calves are relaxed.
- Your ankles and top of your feet, your big toes and all your toes, the soles of your feet are relaxed. All your body is totally relaxed as it sinks deeper into the surface beneath you.
- Imagine now you are at the top of the hill overlooking a wonderful view of the ocean, you can see the waves crashing down and smell the sea on the air, you can hear the waves as they lap onto the beach. The sun is shining, the sky is blue, the sea is a wonderful turquoise colour.
- In front of you, there are some trees and a path through them that will take you to the beach. You begin to follow the path through the trees.

It becomes cooler and darker as you walk through the undergrowth and the trees. You feel the grass brush against your legs as you walk further down the path.

- Eventually, you come to the beach. The sand is golden and warm. You take off your shoes and walk barefoot on the warm sand down towards the sea.

- Your bare feet meet the ocean as it laps on the shore. It feels cool and refreshing. You watch the sea as it laps in and out of the shore.

- You lift your gaze to the sky and see a white fluffy cloud and it seems to be spelling out the letters C A L M. It begins to move towards you until it is directly above you.

- As you breathe out gazing up at the cloud, you see all your cares and worries lift up as if in a balloon and the cloud above becomes dark. Your cares and worries are lifted away, up, up and far away out to sea and off out of the atmosphere. This dark cloud has been lifted far away.

- You feel lighter and happier and carefree. You turn and begin to walk back up the beach, back up the path through the trees, back up to the top of the hill where you feel on top of the world. Lighter, carefree and happy. You take these feelings with you and bring yourself back into the room. Feeling nicely relaxed, refreshed and ready to open your eyes and continue with your day. Or if it is night time, you feel ready to turn over and go to sleep. You have a long, deep, restoring sleep and wake in the morning feeling refreshed.

Authors of the book *The 12 Week Year*, Brian P. Moran and Michael Lennington, say the prefrontal cortex of the brain lights up when you stand and look out over open vistas. When you focus on a compelling future it overcomes the amygdala in the brain (the oldest part of the brain, also known as the limbic or reptile brain) where fear is housed. It's the part that wants to keep us safe small and locked into our emotions of fear.

So, if all else fails and you are still not able to lift your emotional state, go and find a beautiful view and gaze out into the horizon. Walking in nature is also known to have therapeutic benefits. It helps us to be more grounded, and a walk does wonders to lift our spirits. Depression hates movement, so it's a good way to beat the blues.

10) Journaling

Journaling is one of the best ways to get something out of your head and onto paper. It's a private and safe place for you to be honest about your feelings. Here you can offload your grief, sadness, anger and all those other emotions you are dealing with. This helps you get it out and down on paper and helps you release feelings of grief and anger. Once it is on paper it becomes lesser and you become slightly distanced from it. You can then read it through at least three times for it to almost become the third person. A client told me she healed from her miscarriage simply by journaling and writing. She is now writing a book about her miscarriage story and working with Tommy's Charity. You may not want to write a book, but I highly recommend journaling about your feelings that come up.

A gratitude diary is also recommended, perhaps this is something you could try to add into your journaling slowly. I understand it might not be easy to find things to be grateful for when you are post-miscarriage. You can start by being grateful for the roof over your head, the food you ate, the small thing your partner did that touched you and the more you think about it and are aware the more you will find to be grateful for.

Robert Emmons, a leading gratitude researcher from the University of California, Davis, has conducted multiple studies on the link between gratitude and wellbeing. His research confirms that gratitude effectively increases happiness and reduces depression. It's worth doing and will help you feel better and I feel anything to raise the spirits is worth a try.

11) Write a Letter

Another way of getting your feelings out is to write a letter to your baby. "Dear Baby, I miss you, I love you. I know you came for a short time but during that time know you were loved..." Write down what you'd love to tell your baby. Your sorrow, your joy when you found out you were pregnant, and anything that comes to mind. It can help you when you communicate your feelings to the precious baby you lost.

12) META-Health Philosophy

META-Health is an interesting philosophy and many of you won't have heard of it. I certainly hadn't until I met Jo Trewartha, one of the UK's leading META-Health coaches. Knowing that many people search for answers and explanations around their miscarriage, I thought this information could provide a valuable insight for you. Jo explains further:

Miscarriage and Loss ~ A META-Health® Perspective

What is META-Health®?

META is a Greek prefix meaning above and beyond and describes something self-reflective. In a nutshell, META-Health® is a comprehensive bio-psycho-social approach to understanding wellness based on the specific connection between the brain, and a relay system with bodily organs and tissues. META-Health® has developed and evolved from several other approaches; modern medicine and alternative, and is in part science-based and part philosophy. It's revolutionary because the model can be used to explain why we have symptoms when we do. In META-Health® we believe that ultimately nature doesn't make mistakes or errors. Our innate intelligence has made us highly evolved and sophisticated. What we label as illness can be understood as spiritually meaningful and survival orientated. In fact, the body is always trying to heal itself. Our challenge and work are to grow in awareness and transform ourselves. It's both profound and beautiful because our healing journey is our evolution. Working with our mind, emotions, feelings and the body, acceptance and peace can be achieved through consciousness, forgiveness and letting go.

An Explanation for Miscarriage

If you're reading Jo's book because you've experienced miscarriage directly then I firstly wish to say sorry for your loss, and secondly, having worked with Jo I absolutely know that you are in safe hands with her. Everyone's personal life story is different. However, we also know it's not unusual following a miscarriage to experience a whole host of challenging emotions. If applied, the information contained within this book and/or Jo's mentoring and extensive skill set will certainly be beneficial in getting you into a good place on an emotional level.

What I am going to share with you here involves analysing your personal timeline of life events. It will be necessary to think about what was happening prior to the miscarriage. It's important to work through this and it may be initially emotionally painful. Doing so is particularly pertinent should you wish to conceive again in future. Through empirical research and thousands of case studies within META-Health®, we know that there are certain patterns connected to stress, subjective worldview and life experience that tend to occur in those who experience miscarriage which is expressed through the mind-body connection.

Ultimately, I hope to bring you clarity, understanding and peace to enable you to move forward from where you are now if you currently feel that you are suffering because of your loss. Acknowledgement and acceptance of miscarriage can take time, but with sensitive insight and total trust, we can appreciate that at the highest level the pregnancy loss is not a mistake but a meaningful and resourceful natural response. Ultimately, on a soul level, the miscarried baby wasn't ready to be born into the world at this time. All is well on the spiritual plane. As poet Henry Scott Holland wrote, "there is absolute unbroken continuity". Love is real and everything in this universe is but one. We all come from and return to the same source.

As an aside, do remember there are examples everywhere of women who have miscarried going on to have healthy pregnancies, birth experiences and children. If you are feeling worried that you'll never have a longed-for child—maintain hope. Anxiety will not serve you. Let go, life is truly beautiful, magical and miraculous.

Huge love and thanks are extended to Renata Dosangh at www.renatadosanjh.com who is also trained in META-Health® and contributed her understanding, wisdom and insight into this section.

Approximately half of miscarriages occur because of chromosome abnormalities in the foetus. The baby doesn't make it because of damage to DNA. In addition to genetics, we are also concerned with epigenetics which are heritable changes in genetic function linked in with lifestyle and expression of environment, carried and expressed within generations of a family.

It is worth noting that the mother's eggs actually form whilst in her own mother's womb; baby girls are born with their entire number of eggs, whilst sperm in the male partner continues to be produced throughout life. As babies are essentially a combination of both parents we recommend also paying attention to the father's lifestyle and generational history too, prior to conception. It can be profound to send energy healing to past ancestors. Grief, despair and loss are commonly associated past emotional themes, which appear to contribute to miscarriage.

Other reasons for miscarriage include a blighted ovum, where the sac grows but the embryo doesn't, and molar pregnancy where the placenta grows so rapidly that there's insufficient space for the embryo to grow and develop. With regard to blighted ovum, exploring the theme of safety is key. Is it presently safe to have a baby in your current environment? With molar pregnancy it's useful to review how you feel you can provide for a baby; are there economic concerns, for instance?

Furthermore, there can be issues such as ectopic pregnancy where the egg grows in the wrong place, often the fallopian tube. Ectopic pregnancies generally occur when another health issue is present such as endometriosis or pelvic inflammatory disease. This type of miscarriage tends to happen when the mother has previously undergone a period of stress with a survival theme, for instance, losing a person or a sexual trauma.

A further reason for miscarriage is anatomical problems, for example, the cervix is the wrong shape, or even weak, and it dilates too early in the pregnancy to make the birth viable. If this has been an issue for you we encourage you to explore confidence. How do you feel with regards to sex? Do you feel you have the disposition to be a good parent?

Other health conditions affecting the mother can also mean that going full-term is more challenging including infections, diabetes, high blood pressure and underlying thyroid issues. Naturally, regular consultation and frequent monitoring with health care providers are more essential than ever during pregnancy. Coaching sessions, such as those offered by Jo Tocher or a META-Health® professional, can support your mindset around managing a long-term health condition during pregnancy.

Here is some additional interesting information. Following an emotionally charged profound loss or conflict, change occurs within the ovaries. A necrosis can take place, which in turn is connected with a decrease in the female hormone oestrogen. This can lead to the absence of menstruation. Simply, it's not possible to become pregnant at this time. A cyst in the ovary may also be diagnosed. Nature is clever and upon resolving the conflict of profound loss there will be an increase in oestrogen which biologically serves the purpose of making the woman look younger and more attractive. Her libido is also likely to be higher so that the chances that she becomes pregnant are greatly increased. This example again illustrates the importance of resolving difficult emotions.

There are often stories of ladies who have gone on to conceive naturally following IVF and many years of struggle to become pregnant or to carry a pregnancy to term. A logical reason for this could be that they have emotionally resolved the profound loss they experienced and so nature can now sustain the pregnancy.

Clearly, the most traumatic miscarriages are those that occur in later pregnancy. The uterus' smooth muscles help push the baby out during birth. If a lady experiences a significant life event, which causes her to devalue herself as a woman, problems may arise in the uterus. Examples of this type of conflict may even include an initial struggle to conceive or could be associated with unresolved feelings about a previous termination, for example. Another reason may be relationship difficulties between the potential parents. Any potential stressor, abuse or loss could create problems during pregnancy. It's of paramount importance that as human beings we hold a strong sense of self-esteem and self-worth. We're always worthy of self-love.

In a META-Health® analysis and exploration we would be looking to explore beliefs around why, on some level, the mother feels unable to nourish the pregnancy and bring the child into the world or, from the unborn child's perspective, why it may not be optimal to live at this time. Once the reason(s) have been uncovered and identified I recommend doing some EAM® to transform the unhelpful beliefs uncovered. Certainly, be kind to you. There is no fault or blame to be found in the situation. The pregnancy loss was the right outcome at the time it occurred.

The META-Health® Analysis/Timeline for Miscarriage

The following steps explain the natural process that occurs linking the mind and body during a phase of illness. It is a generic map but applies to later stage miscarriage.

Step 1 – Health is in balance.

Step 2 – A life event happens which is unexpected, dramatic and isolating for which the individual feels they have no strategy to deal with the situation. For miscarriage, on some level, there is an underlying reason as to why it's possibly not in the highest good for the baby to live. We call this a stress trigger.

Step 3 – The person then experiences a stress phase they may obsess about the problem.

Step 4 – The worrying stops as a resolution to the problem thinking presents.

Step 5 – The body shifts from the sympathetic nervous system, fight and flight to parasympathetic nervous system rest and digest and regeneration.

Step 6 – The healing peak, this is the part of the cycle where pregnancy loss occurs.

Step 7 – The body begins to return to normal.

Step 8 – The process completes.

Step 9 – Health returns.

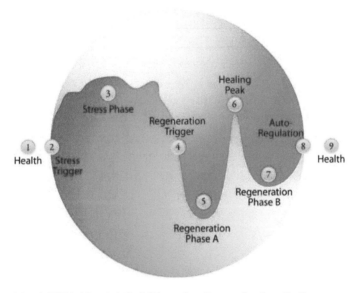

My META-Health® Lifestyle Prescription® for you is please don't suffer in silence following your miscarriage. Reach out and work through any unresolved emotions. Give yourself time physically and emotionally to move on. Remember that most women who miscarry go on to have healthy births in the future. I send you love and wish you all the best for your healing journey and the future.

Jo Trewartha

META-Health® Trainer and Lifestyle Prescriptions® Trainer and Health Coach

www.freeyourmindsolutions.com

Conclusion

There are many strategies which can help you to heal after your loss and I hope this chapter has given you a good overview of techniques that can help. Take the ones that resonate with you most and try them out. I understand that in the early days after a loss it's not easy to think of doing these things, but there will come a time when you are ready for self-help. It's part of self-love and if there's any time you need love it's after a loss. There are many more therapies available and I strongly advise you to go and seek them out. Please, please, please don't just keep calm and carry on. This grief needs to be released and there are many ways in which to do so. You will find that if your grief isn't released that it will bubble up again, time after time until you have no option but to deal with it.

I've recently had a woman come to see me on the thirtieth anniversary of losing her baby who was stillborn and, in those days there weren't many options. She wasn't given the option of saying goodbye to her baby, the baby was taken away and 'dealt with'. The matter was taken out of her hands and she was left, devastated and trying to get on with life. She believes this was the seat of all her physical problems that have resulted in later life. She wanted once and for all to release the energy around this and we had three EAM sessions in which she let go of stuck energy and grief from that time. Emotions are energy in motion and are easy to let go of when you know how. It's when they get stuck and start to pull you in a downward spiral that physical and emotional and mental manifestations happen.

"Health is the greatest gift, contentment the greatest wealth, faithfulness the best relationship."

— *Buddha*

Chapter 4: Healing with Your Partner

There's no denying that experiencing a miscarriage can affect your relationship. As much as you are suffering your partner is suffering too. Women have told me their partners just don't feel the same way. The fact is they can't. They haven't carried the baby, they don't have the hormones coursing through their bodies, nor do they have the physical effects and even though they feel the loss they simply cannot feel it on the same emotional level as a woman who has carried her baby.

It can be a difficult time between couples and if you are able to communicate your worries, fears and anxieties to each other and be totally honest with each other, it will help. It is when someone is thinking something and not saying it and the other is thinking something else, that the problems can arise. Be honest, gentle and considerate of your partner and don't expect too much of each other. You may well feel very different after experiencing miscarriage and even shut down sexually. Your male partner may not totally understand this and take it as rejection. Be prepared to have an honest and open conversation about how you feel in order to pre-empt this. Reassure him that in time you will come to feel your normal self again.

Be aware that your partner may also be feeling that their loss doesn't count, that it doesn't matter as much, because you were the one carrying the baby. I've often heard that they can feel left out, so make sure you take the time to acknowledge their grief too.

I interviewed two relationship coaches and asked them for their advice post-miscarriage. Wendy Capewell, Relationship Specialist, says this:

"Having a miscarriage can be a greatly emotional and painful time for couples. Whilst it's no-one's fault it can leave many questions unanswered, often leading to feelings of guilt, blaming yourself or each other. Whilst your partner is the one person who will really understand your feelings and that can bring couples closer to each other. Being able to share the same cycle of emotions often associated with grief, denial, anger, guilt, feelings of emptiness and longing. Others may become more distant, at least in the short-term, finding it hard to talk to each other about it.

"Because anger is one of the stages of the grieving process, you may find your anger misdirected at each other, leading to constant bickering or arguing. So, you can see why it's important to recognise why you are

angry. On the other hand, you may shrink into your shell, scared of voicing your raw feelings or saying the wrong thing in case you upset your partner, not knowing what to say. But by talking to each other you will allow yourself to grieve and experience all of your feelings, however painful, it's much healthier and helps the grieving process.

It's really important to acknowledge and talk about the fact that you will each likely handle your feelings about the miscarriage differently and not expect too much of yourself or each other, accepting that each of you may take longer to grieve and heal. By being kind and compassionate to yourself and each other, sharing your feelings is likely to strengthen and deepen your relationship and connection with each other.

"You may find it hard to become intimate and the body needs to heal after a miscarriage, so be sensitive to each other and at the same time have cuddles and enjoy each other."

Shelley J. Whitehead, Relationship, Dating and Bereavement Expert, www.shelleywhitehead.com says this:

"HOW A MISCARRIAGE AFFECTS A RELATIONSHIP

Harriet and Steve sat in my consultation room, one sunny morning in July. I listened to Harriet, as her tears fell, recalling the previous four months since the loss of their baby.

Steve sat silently, holding her hand. This lovely couple were struggling, each in their own way, at dealing with a miscarriage. Even the strongest relationship can experience huge challenges following such a loss.

GRIEF EXPRESSED DIFFERENTLY

When Steve spoke, he mentioned that he just wanted his wife back. He was feeling angry and isolated, as she no longer wanted to discuss her feelings with him and was very withdrawn when it came to sexual intimacy.

Harriet said that while this loss was the only thing constantly on her mind, she just felt that Steve wasn't able to hear about her pain. He kept telling her to focus on the future. She had spent every day thinking and dreaming of the little life growing inside her. The excitement mounted when she had her first scan and heard their baby's heartbeat. That future was the reality that occupied her daily thoughts. The dreams were shattered the day that she was informed their baby had died in utero.

It was clear that this couple had different ways of grieving. While Harriet was feeling that life was far from normal, Steve was wondering why it was taking her so long to move on.

She was caught up in the obsessive cycle of thoughts about the baby she was longing for. The anxiety and tension had become a barrier between them, but it was also the catalyst for change.

Research has shown that when couples are not able to talk, they shut down and get trapped in a downward spiral. This couple wisely sought help so they could grow closer and not get stuck.

GRIEF CAN TEAR YOU APART OR BRING YOU CLOSER

Your partner is the one person you may feel safest to discuss your feelings with. If one of the partners feels judged or is not allowed to express their feelings, it can lead to shutting down.

A miscarriage is similar to other forms of bereavement and in some ways, it's also different. If your partner loses a parent or friend, you are able to be the supportive partner. When you lose a baby, you are both in a place of loss. You may have different needs and you may express your grief in your own way; it's not right, it's not wrong, but it's often a cause for concern for your significant other and can become contentious.

HOW CAN YOU SUPPORT ONE ANOTHER AFTER A MISCARRIAGE?

- *Couples feel closer when they are able to talk, listen and really hear one another. While this is vital to the strength of your relationship, it is important to get support from family, friends, colleagues and/or a bereavement specialist. Do not use your partner as the only form of support.*

- *Identify what you most need and want from your partner and gently ask them for this. It may be that you need a hug, a distraction or break from the normal daily routine. Perhaps it is the understanding that your grief may take more time than that of your partner.*

- *Create time to speak about how you feel, using 'I' language. Talk about what you are feeling and going through. While speaking about how you feel is important to keep the communication flowing, speaking about it all the time will lead to disconnection.*

- *Keep these four destructors out of your relationship:*
  - *Criticism*
  - *Blame*
  - *Defensiveness*
  - *Shutdown or passive-aggressive behaviour*

- *Accept that you will be triggered by life in general and specific situations involving babies, pregnancy and the occasions or celebrations around them. A close friend of mine was unable to accept any invitations to baby showers after her miscarriage. Feelings of jealousy and sadness consumed her until she eventually conceived again. Feelings of loss and sadness may be amplified as the birth date approaches.*

- *It might also help to speak to other parents who've experienced the pain of miscarriage. There are many groups, sites and forums where you can connect to them.*

- *Grow in love and work on your relationship. This is a good time to discover more about one another in relation to loss. Ask your partner how loss was dealt with in his family? Tell him how your family handled loss.*

- *If you feel like a barrier has come between the two of you, consult a relationship specialist who can facilitate the process of building the bond of safety, trust and love.*

A miscarriage will define and refine your relationship, but most importantly, you have the power and the choice to let it influence your life in a positive and supportive way."

Women have told me their stories of their partner's behaviour and I've found they mostly fall into the following four categories. You may recognise some or all of them!

Four Common Partner Responses

1. **The Giver** - Fantastic support from your partner who is loving, caring and empathetic to your needs. Is always there for you asking you what you need from them. If this is your partner, then you're one of the lucky ones. In my experience, this can be rare and it shows you have the support, love and understanding from the person who loves you—this is unconditional love and something each of us aspires too. Sadly, this isn't always the case. One of my clients has had continuing, wonderful support from her partner as they both have processed their loss together and grown stronger because of it. She says communication between each other was key.

2. **The Solver** – Most men are programmed to solve problems and find solutions. They often want to jump in and try to fix a scenario by saying things like "let's try again soon" which is often the last thing you want to hear because you wanted THIS baby. They are trying to be

helpful, but sometimes it's not perceived that way. They are trying to 'fix' the situation and the issues that arise around it.

3. **The Feeder** – They feel awkward, not knowing what to do or say but desperately wanting to do something and quite often, that's via food. Buying you your favourite food to cheer you up and showing their love through 'objects', for example, food, alcohol, flowers, chocolate or gifts. They want to 'feed' you, to make you feel better and this is the only way they know how to do it. This was my partner. He tried, but really didn't know how to behave even though he was suffering too.

4. **The Evader** – The Evader doesn't deal with it at all, runs away, is absent, often goes to meet the boys for a drink or play a round of golf. Anything to get out of the house and away from the situation. One client told me that when she came back from the hospital with her husband, she looked out the window and saw him putting his golf clubs in the boot of the car. She felt totally unsupported, angry and alone. This started her downward spiral of depression and she consequently decided that life was not worth living. She had her mother staying at the time, which might have contributed to her partner's swift departure. The doctor was called and she was put on antidepressants which helped her out of the black hole at the time. However, it took her seven more years to come off them again.

Sometimes you just need an instant fix to bring you back up and antidepressants are effective in that way. The downside is that you can become reliant on them and they suppress your feelings, so quite often you feel 'even' or 'numb'. No highs or lows. It is something that doctors offer readily, so do your research on whether you want to go down that route.

After I lost my baby, my partner really didn't know what to do or how to behave. He was a man who wasn't used to not being in control and would often show his emotions or frustrations through outbursts. At this time, he didn't know how to comfort me and in hindsight, it would have been better if I had communicated what I needed. Foremost in my mind, was that I didn't want him to be more upset by seeing me upset, so I did hold myself back from showing him how I grieved. I needed and wanted time and space on my own and he was good about letting that happen. He wanted to feed me and buy all my favourite foods. I have noticed that this is his default pattern as and when adversity strikes since this time. We struggled through and came out the other end stronger.

Five Ways to Support Your Partner to Support You

How do men grieve? Sadly, not very well according to a survey I recently conducted. It concluded that 95% of men had little or no support during this time and none of them were offered counselling, although some said if they'd asked for it at work it would have been provided. In general, they just got on with it and often floundered and were at a loss as to how to comfort their partners or know what to say. My survey also uncovered that a shocking 85% didn't speak to anyone and the 15% who did, felt they didn't get enough support from their mates simply because they either didn't understand what they were going through or just didn't know what to say. "Better luck next time mate," doesn't really cut it.

How can you support your partner to support you?

- Tell him what you need. You may need to be alone, or to cry in his arms; whatever it is you need to communicate that. This is something I found quite difficult, I just wanted to be alone in the bedroom and howl into the bed. I didn't want to cry in his arms because it felt too vulnerable and I knew he couldn't handle seeing me that way. However, after speaking to other women, they told me that often when they had cried in front of their partner, he responded really well and it created softness between them. She had shown her vulnerability—something that's often not easy to do.

  You could say: "Thank you for supporting me, I appreciate you and sometimes I'm going to need you beside me and other times I need to release this grief on my own." "I really need you to hold me right now, I need to be close to you as I grieve."

"I know this is tough for you too, and I need you to not expect too much from me while I heal. Please know that I love you and in time I will be my old self again. I need your love, support and understanding as I work this through."

- Tell him how you feel. Tell him the emotions you're feeling, since he can't guess and explain to him why you're feeling that way. What does it mean to you? For example:

"I'm sad because we have lost our child, I'm sad because you'll never get to take this child to watch football or take them to the park." "I'm feeling scared that this might happen to us again – I'm worried about that." "I'm fearful that we may not be able to have children." "I feel guilty that this is somehow my fault."

We go through a myriad of different emotions after a miscarriage at any given time and although having to tell them how we feel is often painful, it will be worth it to get their support and understanding. Remember that they will understand your emotions academically, but explaining the scenarios to them will deepen their understanding of what you're going through.

- Explain to them what is happening physically in your body so he is aware. You might be bleeding for quite some time afterwards if you have let the miscarriage happen naturally. You may also be tender if you've had a D&C. He needs to know this so that he can understand what you're coping with. Let them know when you are feeling ready to have sex again. If this takes a while to get back to your usual status let them know, so they don't feel rejected by you.

"Please know that I still find you sexually attractive, however, I'm not ready to make love until I heal physically and emotionally. I'm looking forward to getting back to our usual sex-life."

If he suggests you try again soon and you're not ready then explain to him that you need time to grieve this loss before contemplating another— your body needs time to heal. A lot of women have mentioned that their partner is desperate to replace what was lost, but they can't begin to imagine doing that as it's way too soon. It took me three years and a lot of healing to feel ready to try again. Everyone is different in this regard and some may feel ready to try again after a couple of months. In this instance you could say:

"I love that you'd like to try again and right now I can't begin to contemplate this because I need to heal and grieve from THIS loss. I would love to try for another baby when the time is right."

- Explain that you may need to talk to your girlfriends and have support from them, as well as family. Encourage them to get support by either talking to their mates or having counselling. This is in no way to diminish their role, it's just that you often need to grieve with your girlfriends and have an outside perspective.

"I feel like I'd love to spend some time talking this through with the girls and you probably need a night out with your mates?"

Conclusion

If you find that your relationship is not what it was before your pregnancy loss then it really is worth considering couples counselling. It can help to have a third party who is outside of the situation to help you come together again and work through what is coming up. If your needs and those of your partner aren't met, this is where the cracks begin to show. Communication is key here.

Sometimes if your relationship isn't strong to begin with, a miscarriage can be the deal breaker. A common emotion felt is shame. Shame to have failed to produce a baby, shame that your body has let you down. Childbirth is a primal instinct, an inherent calling that most women want to fulfil and when this fails our emotions can run riot. It can also bring up anger between couples. Feelings of anger towards each other, especially if they feel they've not been supported. Blame plays a big part too. The blame of self and blame of your partner. The story of my client whose husband went off to play golf when they got home from the hospital, says this was the beginning of the end for their relationship. It took a few years after but they are now divorced. It was the beginning of a slippery slope for them.

In some cases, in hindsight, it can be a relief to a woman or her partner to have a miscarriage because their relationship was never going to work. Hindsight is a wonderful thing and can throw up some incredible insights that are rarely felt or seen at the time of a traumatic event.

Conversely, it can strengthen your relationship. It bonds you together and you grow stronger because of it. You pull together to make it work, respecting the feelings of each other and by communicating in a calm way about each other's needs.

Whatever you are feeling and going through, remember to communicate and if you get to a point where you don't know how it's going to evolve, my advice is to seek professional help.

"There is no greater agony than bearing an untold story inside you."

— *Maya Angelou*

Chapter 5: Family, Friends and Loved Ones

Relationships can be difficult to navigate on the whole. It's not always easy to speak about your loss with your friends and family. I found myself supporting them mostly, as I didn't want them to be upset. It was fine to talk about in the beginning, but after a while, they stopped asking how you are and more or less expect you to get on with it. So, you sweep it under the carpet and don't talk about it often. Occasionally, a close friend will ask how you are which is nice and I found myself being honest in those circumstances. People are awkward around grief and loss, I know I was before my loss because I just didn't know what to say or how to say it.

I have now learnt to ask the person how they are and if there's anything they need from me. Sometimes people don't always want to talk about it and that's their prerogative, asking the question makes them feel a little supported and makes them feel you care. I was also pleasantly surprised by people who took the time to write a card, send a message, phone or send me flowers or chocolates. It was very touching and very much appreciated.

On the other hand, it could be disappointing when those you thought might reach out didn't and this is something I hear of from a lot of women. They feel disappointed and let down by the people they thought might have been there for them and weren't. It is difficult to process, it's hurtful and, unfortunately, it's another thing to deal with emotionally. You may feel a range of emotions around this: hurt, anger, frustration, sorrow and blame. Otherwise known as the pointy-finger scenario. Try to acknowledge them and let them go as best you can so that you can start to heal.

In the following pages, I speak about different scenarios you might face with your friends, family and your existing children, should you have them. There may be similar incidences that you have come across and it is my hope that you can take something from it and learn something new so you can address the situation, rather than let it simmer. When we let something simmer it drains our energy and slows down our healing process.

Children

If you already have children you might have let them know that they are going to have a baby brother or sister soon. Your child was most probably excited about this and then you had a miscarriage. So how do you handle the relationship with your children around this?

It can push many buttons for you. How do I explain to my child that their brother or sister is not going to be born? Of course, it depends on what age they are but in all ages, honesty is the key.

I interviewed my friend and EAM colleague, Karen Shaw, who is a parenting specialist, coach and NLP practitioner of Parenting Magic. She is an expert in her field with an amazing insight into words and how to express to children in a way they will understand and be able to assimilate. She says:

"Having a miscarriage or losing a baby is a very difficult, sad and life-changing experience. When you already have children or a child, you have also to deal with how it affects them and how you are going to tell them. One of my passions as a parenting coach is enabling parents to communicate in a positive and conscious way as so often we don't really think too much about what we are saying and the effect it can have upon our children. For example, I have referred to miscarriage as 'losing a baby' as it often is. If we think for a minute what that might mean to a young child, it isn't very accurate nor does it make sense. They might be wondering 'how?' or 'where from?'

What you say or tell other children will depend on what you have already told them, or what they already know. If you haven't said anything and they didn't know, what they will know and pick up on is your energy, your emotions, mood, etc. They will know something has happened, something has changed;

they sense it. Your electromagnetic field, the energy you are emitting will be of a different frequency and they will feel it. If we don't explain that something has happened and we are feeling sad, want to be quiet and may cry sometimes, they may start to wonder if it's them that has caused this. They can blame themselves and not tell you that!

If they knew they were going to have a baby brother or sister, then tell them, the baby we were expecting, won't be able to come now. Sometimes they accept things without asking too much. Only answer what they ask. If they ask why not, explain it as honestly as you can in a way they will understand. If they understand death and have experience of it, say the baby died or say that if they can grasp the concept. It means not alive and not coming back. Euphemisms aren't helpful and can cause more fear and problems. If you say the baby has fallen asleep and won't wake up again, that could cause them to fear sleep.

Reassure them it's nothing they did, they didn't cause it to happen, children can blame themselves and think that maybe something they did (naughty in their mind) has caused it. Reassure them that you love them very much and just need time to be sad. Understand that they may not dwell on the news and after being told and may want to go back to 'normal' as they do not feel as you do, nor are they experiencing your emotions. Make sure they know they can talk to you about how they feel and what they are thinking. They could be wondering if that baby has died, might they? Could it happen to them? Keep a dialogue going.

It's important to carry on with as much of the normal routine as possible and still do things that were planned when the baby arrived, or they may feel they are being punished. They need to know they are valued, important, that they matter and are loved."

I recently met a woman, Eileen, who told me her mother went into hospital to have her younger baby brother or sister. There was a lot made about it and her mother was clearly excited. However, the baby died during childbirth and never came home. Eileen was three years old and was waiting for this baby to come home and it never did. Her mother didn't explain what had happened and Eileen kept on waiting. Her mother, constantly referred to the baby and over time Eileen began to resent this baby who was so important to her mother and began to feel like she didn't matter at all. This was the start of a difficult relationship she had with her mother for the years following.

Now you have Karen's valuable information, you have the tools to address this situation in a conscious way.

You may find yourself overcompensating with your children or giving them more to make up for the loss of your baby. You could also be overprotective and worried that something may happen to them. Try to keep the relationship on an even keel as your child will pick up your worry and angst and in turn take it on as they will feel the energy of how you're feeling. They will have enough of their own feelings to process and it's difficult for them to take on more.

Family Members

Family members can either be lovely or slightly disappointing around your loss. Family tend to be quite blunt with each other and this can often erupt in arguments. My family were far away in New Zealand, so I communicated to them via telephone and when I did go and visit they were wonderfully supportive. One of my sisters asked me to be godmother to her first-born son, which was a lovely gesture and one I appreciated immensely at the time.

Usually, you'll find that parents and siblings are supportive. The awkward dynamic, which can arise is if your sibling announces they are pregnant in a short space of time after your loss. This is hard; you want to feel happy for them but at the same time can be devastating news for you.

I hear this time and time again from the women I work with and it's not an easy situation to reconcile yourself with. In the case of a family member or a friend, it's okay to give yourself permission to take time away and have your own space. Make the choice that you won't see that person until you feel ready to. Give yourself the space and the gift of time to heal. You may be wondering how to do this or thinking your friend or sister won't understand. Try to have a chat and let them know that, although you are delighted for them, you're still hurting and it's going to take some time and that it is in your best interest to take some space for yourself and you'll be back when it's less raw.

I would also advocate taking a digital detox. Often, we are on social media and we see things that are upsetting and the last thing you would need to see is that someone else is pregnant. When you are in a better place, then you can rejoin the world of social media.

I would also suggest, taking time away from watching soaps and the news. I've found, quite often, storylines in soaps can be depressing and there are always disasters reported in the news. When we hear this, we can spiral further down into depression, fear and sadness and it can take us longer to come back up from these lower vibrating emotions to a feeling of neutral and eventually happiness. Ask yourself, do I really need to be watching this? Is it going to make me feel better or worse?

Conversely, do watch uplifting and inspiring films, documentaries or comedies also read books which will make you feel better and get you into a place where you feel at least calm and content, if not happy.

Friends

Time and time again I hear from my clients that they feel disappointed by the reaction of a friend. It's interesting that this often comes up and it's interesting that it can be a friend who you are surprised by, someone you wouldn't expect to act that way. One of my clients said she had always supported her friend through everything and when she was pregnant her friend was elated and in constant contact. As soon as she lost her baby everything changed. She avoided her and didn't even pick up the phone to have a conversation. It was as if she couldn't handle the change in the friendship dynamic. She was the one who always needed the support and when that changed she couldn't handle it or be there. This can be hard to bear and is extremely hurtful. I was lucky enough not to experience this and each one of my friends was there for me in their own way.

Sometimes this happens to highlight that the person is not as you thought and maybe it was a toxic friendship or one-sided. They were drawing on what you had to give them. They were a taker, someone who took what they needed from the friendship but wasn't giving much back. It often happens with those friendships that are the 'fun' friendships: someone who is great fun to go out with and have a good laugh with. Quite often there is a payoff such as generosity but when the chips are down and in times of travesty these things are often highlighted, so you can have a rethink about your friendships. If something is particularly surprising, approach the person and explain how you felt when they were absent. They might be mortified and let you know that they didn't know how to behave around you in the circumstances.

I'm not a fan of having people around me who don't serve me and don't have my best interests at heart. It's taken me a few years to realise this as when younger, I would 'put up' with friendships that I didn't enjoy because I didn't like confrontation of any sort or letting people down. Now, I'm more confident about putting myself first. The saying that people come into your life for a reason (usually to teach you something), a season (just for a short period to serve a purpose) or for a lifetime is rather freeing, and helped me understand that it was okay not to hang onto friendships that were controlling, toxic or just not enjoyable anymore.

Very recently, Diana told me about her best friend who lost her baby. They've had a relationship since they were children where they talked about everything personal and shared what was important to each other. At the time she lost her baby (a still-born) Diana was there for her, however, since then, it had become the elephant in the room. It's something in twenty-eight years that has never been talked about between them. Diana hasn't mentioned it because she's awkward around it and her friend hasn't mentioned it either. It's a big unspoken, heavy energetic ball that is always there between them.

Diana also grieved when her best friend's baby died because she was hoping to be godmother and was excited about the impending arrival of her friend's baby. Diana doesn't have children of her own, so this meant a lot to her.

Her friend doesn't know how she feels about this and I suggested that they sit down and broach the subject. It's the holding of this elephant that is draining. It sucks your energy, it holds you back and it wears you down. I'm looking forward to hearing the outcome.

If this relates to you in any way, do take the initiative and ask your friend how they are feeling about things. They may not want to open up and talk about it, but they may open up a crack and when the crack is open it becomes wider and wider and eventually, it will all come out. Letting your friend know that you're here for them in anyway is key. If you are the one who has lost the baby, also let your friend know how you're feeling because it is likely that she is afraid of upsetting you, so hasn't mentioned it for that reason.

Please Don't Ask Me When I'm Going to Have Another Child

This question is laden with unseen, unheard and unanswered responses and it is one that can be flung around without thought. It is something that a woman who has lost her baby dreads to hear. I discovered that I began to answer with a smile on my face telling the questioner that I would love to have more children, but that right now it's not happening. People would then realise that their question, asked without thought, was multi-layered.

However, it is something that many of us hear, many times and when we are feeling sensitive it can be hurtful. For example, if you met a stranger while out shopping, or in a café and they say, "Have you just got the one child?" You would mainly answer, "Yes, just one." If the question is asked by a friend or a family member then you can go into more depth with the answer and let them know what is happening to you.

When you have a child and then a miscarriage you may incur the feeling from others around you that it's not important because you already have a child. This is extremely hurtful. Having a child certainly doesn't make your miscarriage any less important.

Kate says: "I encountered people's attitude that because I already had a child, my miscarriage didn't matter. It felt like it was disregarded."

The main thing to remember is that people ask questions without thinking of the consequences, or say things that are hurtful without realising. They often have no idea what is going on in your life and sometimes a gentle reminder that it is a thoughtless question would stop them asking someone else.

When You Get Blindsided

This can happen when you're out and about and run into someone you know and they tell you their exciting news they're pregnant. You feel your heart drop to your stomach and become hot and sweaty – this is the same reaction as shock – cortisol is released and expresses as heart palpitations (a racing heart), sweatiness and shortness of breath. You can also feel light-headed.

If this happens to you, I would advise taking a deep breath and exhale deeply to get rid of the excess carbon dioxide (CO_2). Another good strategy to help ground yourself is to press your thumb and middle finger together while taking in a breath. If you have water take a drink and Rescue Remedy (already prepared in the bottle of water will help calm you). Smile and say how happy you are for them and cut the conversation off quickly so you don't have to listen to every detail. "Congratulations, that's great news. It's lovely to see you, I'm on my way to meet someone and I'm late, so have to run now," will save you being stuck for ages when you don't want to be there.

This is a coping strategy you may need to employ a few times, so practice it at home before you go out.

Conclusion

Relationships with friends, family and children can be tricky. The best way to navigate this is to put yourself first. You are the one who has had the devastation in your life, do what is right for you. Try to please yourself first before pleasing other people. Explain how you're feeling to your loved ones—communication really is so important here. People don't know how you're feeling or coping and often hazard at a guess, which can be way off base. Give them a helping hand by letting them know what you need from them. Keep your best support network around you, your tribe, those that love you unconditionally and want the best for you. They will more than likely be your family and some very special friends who show up for you and hold your hand. You know who they are—embrace and appreciate them.

"It is during our darkest moments that we must focus to see the light."

— *Aristotle*

Chapter 6: Going Back to Work

I often get asked the question: When is it the right time to go back to work? The truth is it's different for everyone and you will know in yourself when it's right for you.

Focus on Work

Some people like to get back into their old routine, as it feels like a semblance of normality. Nothing has changed at work—it's familiar. You throw yourself into work to forget the pain, it's time to focus on something totally different than the pain of loss. I get that, and I see that is where most people feel comfortable. I ask you this: if you bury all your pain in work, where does it come out and how is it released? Much like a pressure cooker, it will at some point explode, whether that is in a heap in the bathroom, or a screaming session with your work colleague or at home with your partner. What I'm saying here is that it will come out at some point unless you release it and you'll have no control when that will be, so be prepared.

More Time Off

Others feel they'd like to take more time off work to really be prepared for what lies ahead in the workplace. It can be very delicate as someone can ask you gently how you are and the floodgates open. Give yourself more time if you need to before returning. Make sure you're feeling ready for it, a few more days to recover will stand you in good stead.

I Don't Want to Go Back

Others don't want to go back to work at all. This was me; I found it so difficult to return. I was dreading it and I felt very self-conscious thinking everyone would be looking at me. Of course, most of them weren't; they were too busy doing what they had to do at work! If this is you, take time to think about it. If you're in the position where you don't have to return to work and really, really don't want to, my advice is to follow your heart. If you go back, as I did, your heart might never be in it and at some point, you'll know when the time is right to leave.

I realise that compassionate leave is different for each company you work for and sometimes you don't get a choice, you have to go back to work after a short time.

For those who work for themselves and have their own business, there's a different pressure and I know all too well that if you're self-employed, when you don't work, you don't get paid and that there is no compassionate leave. In this case, it is entirely up to you to decide how long you need. My advice is to ease in gently, taking each day as it comes.

I was fortunate enough to work for a very understanding corporate company. We had our funeral ten days after I had delivered our baby boy John. I then felt a compelling need to go home. My home was in New Zealand and I was living in London. Neither my partner or I had family in the UK, so it was an isolating time. My support were my friends and they mostly rallied. I felt the need to be around my family and have some TLC and my company were happy to give me more compassionate leave. I took three weeks in total and flew back to New Zealand. It was great being in the bosom of my family and I felt like a child again being loved and cared for. My dad collected me at the airport and on the way home asked if I wanted to have an ice cream. That was our routine when we were kids, we would always stop for an ice cream (mine was always hokey pokey, a kiwi classic) on our car journeys. I still find this emotional, my father a man of few words, showed his love and care in that one sentence: Would you like an ice cream? It still makes me emotional when I think of it.

I came back to work pretty much straight after a long-haul flight, and I basically fell apart. I couldn't seem to function on my first day back and spent a lot of time going to the bathroom to cry. One of the human resources managers must have heard

I was struggling and came to see if I was okay. I fell apart again and she brought me into her office and offered to send me to counselling. Given that my last experience in the hospital was less than brilliant I was quite reluctant, but they more or less said I had to. I ended up going for CBT (Cognitive Behavioural Therapy) and it was quite helpful. I have since discovered I needed more than words or 'mind' therapy to heal. You see we are mind, body and soul and it was my soul that was hurting. I didn't discover this until a year or so later.

My department head was very supportive of my pregnancy, in fact, she called me into her office to congratulate me and have a talk. She was very emotional and I couldn't work out why, as she was definitely not a soft person. However, I subsequently found out that she'd suffered six miscarriages; she had a daughter but was unable to have more children. When I arrived back at work, she came over to my desk and was very cold, she more or less told me to get back to work: 'keep calm and carry on'. This made me feel confused and unsupported and to be honest, I closed down towards her. I managed to stay in the job for about three more months, but my heart wasn't in it. This, the job that I had previously LOVED! The thing was, I was a completely different person. Something had changed in me so intrinsically that it was scary. I felt I didn't fit in, I was a square peg in a round hole. My colleagues were lovely people and I always enjoyed their company and especially the after-work drinks, however, this left me cold and wanting as well.

My soul was crying out for change, I just didn't know what it was. It was when I heard the chief executive giving us an 'inspirational talk' telling us his vision for the company and how he wanted us all to support it, that I had my moment of clarity. This was not MY vision, I wanted something more than this—I just wasn't quite sure of what that was. I decided to resign. I spoke about it with my partner and he was supportive but concerned about what I'd do.

When I left, I took some temporary work as a personal assistant in a software company. It was easy work and I didn't have to stretch myself. I believe that it gave me time to work out what I wanted to do and sure enough when I stepped back out of a situation and just let myself 'be' the answer came because the universe always has your back. I know it doesn't seem like it when you're going through adversity. Hindsight is a wonderful thing and I'd say to any of you that at some point in your life, you will be able to look back and have some clarity around why you suffered your pain and loss.

My clarity about what I was going to do next came one quiet Saturday afternoon as I was flicking through a magazine. I saw a title, 'She Changed her Career and her Life' which grabbed my attention. When I was reading through the article the hairs on the back of my neck stood up and I got goosebumps. I felt as though I was the person in the article, she too, had left a corporate life because she was disillusioned with it, she too had been through adversity, she too was searching for something more. She trained as an aromatherapist and loved it.

At the end of the article, there were contact details advertising a taster weekend. I booked it up immediately. It was at this weekend that I felt I was on the right path. I was so excited and absolutely loved every moment of it. I loved learning about the essential oils and I loved learning massage. I decided to join the school (The Tisserand Institute) and complete a diploma starting the following September.

This was the start of my holistic journey and one I've never looked back from. Over the years, I have gained more knowledge and trained in several different modalities, which are now all part of my toolbox for helping people get through a difficult situation or just feel better! This is my driver, I wanted people to feel better and for me, there is no better way of doing this than giving them a treatment that makes them feel amazing. Something that I still get a kick out of to this day.

I love facilitating change for the better in people's lives. This is my path in life, and you know what, I probably may not have realised it if I hadn't lost my baby boy—I now know that it was an almighty kick up the backside from the universe to get me on my right path. You often come across crossroads in life and think, do I take the left? The road that is well travelled and safe and secure. Or do I take the right? The unknown path, the road that is slightly scary but also exciting. It's here where we all have a choice to make and it shapes your life and wakes you up. Something to think about if you want change in your life if you're feeling stuck and you're tired of feeling that way. It's a bit like groundhog day. If you take the road less travelled it may not always be easy, but it will always be worth it.

When Is It Too Soon or Too Late to Go Back?

Here are some guidelines to know when to return to work:

If you feel:
- Vulnerable
- Broken inside
- Tearful most days
- Unable to cope with anything
- Depressed
- Overwhelmed

Or you have:
- Bleeding
- Pain

Then it is most likely too soon. See if you can get further leave from your company and take more time to heal. You can visit your doctor and get a medical certificate to verify your health, both mentally and physically.

If you feel:
- Restless and bored
- Unable to relax
- Physically well

Or you:
- Need some direction
- Want something else to focus on

Then it's probably time for you to return to work.

However, if you feel:
- Disenchanted about work
- You need a change of direction
- You are not in any hurry to return
- You have a different perspective on life
- You want to give something back

It's probably time for a change. It's time to look for something new, to move on and make new discoveries, whether that is going travelling, retraining, enrolling in a course, finding a new job, volunteering or doing something you've always dreamed of. If you are fortunate enough to be able to take unlimited time to figure this out then take this feeling and run with it; act and start a new journey. There are plenty of new things to discover and my advice is to look into everything you've dreamt about. Something will jump out at you and you'll just know that this is it! It happened to me when I picked up that magazine and read the article about someone very similar to me. It was as if the article was written especially for me. I felt alive for the first time in ages!

How to Handle Colleagues

I would advise when going back to work to communicate to your colleagues how you're feeling.

This is easy if you work closely with someone and already know them well. Not quite so easy if it's a department head. You will find that your colleagues won't know how to be around you and may even ignore you because they don't know what to say. They don't want to upset you by saying the wrong thing, so they say nothing at all which can come across as slightly confusing for you and hurtful, to say the least.

You may also come across the colleague who is brusque and says a thoughtless statement and then continues as if nothing has changed. Or you'll get the ones who think they know what you're going through and say something totally inappropriate. Be prepared for all eventualities and try not to be too upset about it. It's because they have no clue about how you're feeling and what you're going through, and if they haven't experienced a miscarriage or baby loss they really won't be able to empathise.

If you're feeling there is an awkwardness between you and your colleagues then it would be appropriate for you to bring up the subject of your loss by saying, "I know you're probably feeling awkward around me and are unsure of what to say, and this is what I need from you right now." Then you can explain what you need. Also, explain how you might be feeling from time to time. That you may need some time out if you need to cry or you may need to not talk about it and just get on with your work. Whatever is right for you. You'll be going through hormonal changes and will be emotionally up and down, especially if you are still bleeding after a miscarriage. Hopefully, you've given yourself enough time to bleed before going back to work.

There is also the fact if you have miscarried early, then you probably haven't communicated to work that you were pregnant. Your colleagues may not know what is going on for you and you may like to keep it that way. However, if you're struggling I would advise having a chat with those you closely interact with and let them know what is going on.

Communicating With Your Boss

I would strongly recommend having a chat to your boss and letting them know how you're feeling so they can be mindful of it and not expect you to be the same as you were before your miscarriage. You will feel so different but outwardly to everyone else, everything is the same as it was. This should take the pressure off you and your work performance a little.

In hindsight, I wish I had been strong enough to speak about this with my boss. She was very overbearing when I came back and decided that I should carry on as normal, she felt this was what I needed to get me back on the right track. After her many miscarriages, this tactic worked for her, however, we are all different and I felt like a changed person and throwing myself into this job was not my destiny.

When speaking to your boss, prepare what you're going to say before. Make a list and refer to it if you need to. It's very easy to be dismissed by someone, so stay strong, calm and centre yourself. Take nice deep breaths and exhale slowly. Have some Rescue

Remedy to hand and put a few drops into a bottle of water and sip before you go in and during the meeting.

Let them know how you're feeling and what you need in order to get back into your routine. Do tell them you may need more time than usual to feel 'normal' again. Let them know that it is fine (or not) to speak about it or ask questions. Decide how you'd like it to be and what you can cope with. Tell them you are still going through grief and that some days you'll feel strong and other days you won't. If they know what to expect from you, they'll likely be more understanding. Let them know it may take more time than they expect.

Should I Have Therapy?

Yes, yes and yes! It's very important to be able to talk to someone who is neutral about what you've been through. Someone, who is not emotionally invested in you. Someone you can be entirely frank with about how you feel, someone who is not going to judge you. It's cathartic to get it all 'out', it's part of your healing process. If you're an analytical person then counselling or CBT is for you. You can talk it through in an analytical way, you can cry in a safe space and you can begin to heal. Work may offer this and it is worth asking if you could go through the company health plan to get support. Even if you're not analytical, it's good to talk it through with a professional and do bear in mind that you may also need something more than counselling. Healing treatments, such as aromatherapy, acupuncture, hypnotherapy, Reiki or hands-on healing. There are many types of healing you can find, such as ThetaHealing, spiritual healing, a healing circle or group or even psychic healing. Several clients have told me how seeing a psychic was a huge comfort as it made them feel closer to their lost baby and loved ones who had already passed.

How to Support Myself When I Go back?

Firstly, don't expect too much of yourself. You will be feeling more vulnerable and sadder. You will have a lot of hormones coursing through your body, not to mention the emotions! You will also be going through hormonal changes and these can take a while to return to normal after a miscarriage. Physically you may still be bleeding and/or tender and possibly in pain.

Take plenty of supplies into work, such as sanitary towels or a moon cup (if you use one) for the bleeding, something for the pain – (you may need to take an anti-inflammatory painkiller, if you're feeling achy –) and use what you generally use for period pains. Have some Rescue Remedy in your bag and put a few drops in a glass of water—this will help with your emotional and hormonal ups and downs.

I always carry essential oils with me—lavender and geranium are perfect. Pop a drop of each on a tissue and inhale deeply when you need to. The lavender will calm you and the geranium is a balancer, i.e. it balances out your hormones and your emotions.

I'm also a huge fan of homeopathy and have used homeopathic remedies frequently over the years. I would also advise going to see a homeopath and having acupuncture to set your hormones right again. A few of my clients have had acupuncture successfully for fertility which is something to consider if or when you want to try to get pregnant.

Conclusion

Going back to work was one of the most difficult things about my baby loss for me. I felt vulnerable and lonely. I felt no one understood what I'd been through, which actually they can't because they haven't travelled your journey in your shoes.

Going back to work may be an easy transition for you because it's something familiar. It can be good to go back to something that is familiar. It's something you did that was normal before things changed and doing something which is normal can be comforting.

However you feel about it, it's usually got to happen and it's a matter of getting through it the best way you can. It will become easier after a while and some days will be better than others, but know that you will get through it and have some 'learnings' along the way.

"The walls we build around us to keep sadness out also keeps out the joy."

— *Jim Rohn*

Chapter 7: Finding Joy Again

It may seem like an impossible task to find joy again when you've lost your very much-wanted baby, however, there are things we can start to do to help with this process. It is important for you to find your joy again, so you can move through the grief cycle.

Sometimes, we don't know what to do to help ourselves on a practical level. We are so caught up with what is going on inside, with how we are feeling and our emotions. We can become frustrated with that and want to actively do something. We want to do something that feels tangible, so we can take some sort of control over our circumstances and start to feel better.

Three wonderful things you can do to help yourself heal are to think about community, ceremony and contribution. These are three human needs: we like to be part of a community, it provides comfort and security and a feeling of belonging. We like a ceremony to mark an important event, whether that is to celebrate a new life, or to say goodbye to a life. When we contribute, it makes us feel good.

Community

Being part of a community means you don't have to be alone. You are part of something that others may have had similar experiences of. A community where you can be in a safe space with like-minded people who have been through a similar experience of the loss of their baby. The changing emotions of grief can catch us off guard, causing us to act out of character or differently than our typical personality and demeanour. We all need a support system to help us as we move through our grief journey. Family and friends are vital in their support unless they have experienced loss of a pregnancy they most likely don't fully 'get it'. That is where support groups or a community become invaluable. In a support group, you will find new friends also living a life after losing their baby.

These groups offer companionship and understanding from others who have experienced a similar loss and are experiencing similar challenges that living with loss brings. In a culture that often avoids talking about the loss of your baby, support groups give you the opportunity to share your story openly and guilt-free. You also have the opportunity to hear the stories of others and talk about coping day-to-day, as well as on the most difficult days of your grief journey.

If you are looking for a support system in your grief journey, consider joining a support group, whether online or in person.

You will find:

- Emotional support in a safe and non-judgmental environment.
- Support and understanding from others who have experienced a similar loss.
- The opportunity to begin the healing process by sharing your own story and hearing the stories of others.
- Coping skills to help you through the most difficult days.
- Hope through companionship with people who 'get it' and understand first-hand what you're going through.
- Permission to grieve and permission to find acceptance and live a happy and productive life.

Many women have told me they joined one or two support groups and how they found them of comfort, knowing that they were not alone. Hearing that someone else was going through a similar experience was quietly comforting. Quite often, they didn't participate in the group but by just being there, reading the content and hearing what others had experienced was a comfort.

It is definitely worth looking for a community to join, there are plenty on social media and in-person meet up groups available. Some of which I have listed in the Cross-ref to section at the end of this book.

Ceremony

When a person dies there is a funeral and the benefit of having a funeral is to give closure. It's also a crucial part of the grief cycle. It is where people mourn together and remember fondly the person who has died. It's where friends and family congregate to celebrate the life of someone they loved.

When we lose a baby during pregnancy, there is no ceremony unless we decide to have one. I was offered a ceremony by the hospital. It was non-denominational and was simple and lovely. It was something that helped us come to terms with our loss. It was simply my partner and I and the hospital chaplain. It was intimate and personal. I realise when one has an early miscarriage or a miscarriage between 12 and 20 weeks this isn't normally offered. Sometimes, you may be asked if you'd like to keep the remains so you can conduct your own ceremony. Many women feel shocked by this at the time and it all seems rather clinical and perfunctory. However, some in hindsight wished they had taken the remains of their baby so they had something tangible at their ceremony. Do bear in mind that you can still have a ceremony without any remains. It will still mean the same to you.

Having your own ceremony is something I highly recommend and you can do it in many different ways. Here are some suggestions. It is worth bearing in mind, if you elect to miscarry at home you are most likely to lose your baby in the toilet. If at all possible, you can take the remains and do your own burial or whatever feels right for you. One of my clients who elected to have her miscarriage naturally at home told me it took five hours to discharge. The bleeding was intense and painful and she witnessed her foetal remains disappear down the toilet. This is the harsh truth about a natural miscarriage and one that I elected to have also when I lost my second baby at eight weeks. In hindsight both my client and I would have preferred to have a D&C because it is over much quicker. There can be bleeding afterwards, but not to the same extent.

Ideas For a Ceremony

- Hire a celebrant and invite those that you'd love to be there, or have a quiet, personal one with you and your partner and children if you have them. Celebrants are well versed in making a beautiful ceremony and you can decide how you want it.

- Have your own private ritual or ceremony: light a candle, write a poem or write a letter to your baby. This is a lovely way to remember and acknowledge their existence.

- Ask your hospital if you can use their chapel and/or speak to the hospital chaplain. Each hospital will have different regulations around this, however, it is worth asking the question.

- Plant a tree, shrub or your favourite flower in your garden to remember your baby. If you don't have a garden a pot plant will also work.

- Keep a memory box with the scan picture and other things that you may have which remind you. I wrote a poem and read it out at the funeral and now keep it in the memory box with photos the midwife took after my stillbirth.

- Attend a 'Saying Goodbye' service, a UK based charity that provides support to anyone who has suffered the loss of a baby at any stage of pregnancy, at birth or in infancy. They take place across the UK, US (Boston) and France (Paris). See www.sayinggoodbye.org.

Whatever you decide to do, you'll likely find it to be helpful and healing in your grief journey.

Celebrant Jacqui Tillyard from www.yourspecialceremony.co.uk, Your Special Ceremony says this:

"*As a celebrant, it's a very difficult role when it comes to performing a baby life celebration ceremony. Often emotion gets in the way, anything from deep grief to anger, blame, sadness, etc. There are no words adequate, which can come near to soften the tragedy when we are faced with the shock of a miscarriage or unexpected death.*

Yet there is something that can never be taken away, however long or short a life may have been, something which is the best part of any life, the one thing which is remembered above any achievement, and that is the experience of giving and receiving love. There is no doubt at all that so much love flowed from the hearts of those who surrounded the baby, and no doubt at all that they would have responded to this love. The ceremony is the last act of love and respect for which thanks can be given for the joy and contribution the anticipated arrival of the baby ever made.

A woman who loses her husband is called a widow. A man who loses his wife is called a widower. A child who loses their parents is called an orphan. And yet there is no word for a parent who loses a child because there is no word to describe that unbelievable grief that consumes your entire mind and body and soul."

Dear Baby – A Note From Your Mother By Jacqui Tillyard

Oh, my dear lost one,

My sadness is so deep and so wide I feel I would drown in the ocean that was you.

I cannot express enough how much I shall miss you,

The hurt and the regret are hard hurdles to get over, perhaps I never will.

A part of me died when you went away.

What I can say is that I loved you dearly, that I will treasure your memory forever

You will always remain a part of me and me of you,

I will hold on to the joy your anticipated arrival bought to our family

I will hold on to how much you were wanted and loved

Rest now my baby, rest in the arms of the angels, where no harm can come to you.

Conclusion

By having a ceremony, you are closing the chapter and it makes a big difference in the way you heal, and how you feel. It's allowing you to honour your baby for its short life, to honour the way you felt towards your baby and it's something that you will always remember. I would highly recommend you do something, in your own time, and you will know when you are ready. It will make you feel closer to having closure.

Contribution

Contributing to society is something that makes us feel better. When we give to others it raises our spirits. There are many side effects of kindness and giving. In David R. Hamilton's book *The Side Effects of Kindness* he outlines how there are five side-effects of kindness. He says, "Scientific evidence has proven that kindness changes the brain, impacts the heart and immune system, is an antidote to depression and even slows the ageing process. We are genetically wired to be kind, and when we're kind we feel happier and our bodies are healthiest."

Something so simple, with great benefits.

When we contribute to a charity it also makes us feel good. It creates a feeling of gratitude and compassion for others and our appreciation awakens when we give back. There is nothing greater to bring us back to our centre than beginning to understand just how much we have to be grateful for. This is often difficult to see when we are in the midst of our own grief and loss and through contribution, we can start to acknowledge our gratitude and find compassion for others.

When we suffer from adversity, a particular illness or have been affected by a traumatic event, we sometimes feel like we want to give back. It makes us focus on something and feel able to make a difference. This is why some of us enter organised events, such as cycle rides, walks, or run marathons to raise money for various charities that mean something to us. If this is something you are drawn to do, there are some amazing charities in the UK related to miscarriage and pregnancy loss, such as Sands, Tommy's, the Miscarriage Association and Saying Goodbye and the Genesis Research Trust. They are more than happy to have your contribution and if nothing else please do go and check out their websites for lots of great information.

The bottom line is that contributing makes us feel good, it raises our spirits and we begin to feel useful again at a time when we feel so utterly powerless. It focuses the mind on something that is outside of us and makes us feel empowered and more confident.

High Days and Holidays:

One of the most difficult holidays to deal with is Christmas Day, especially if you've recently lost your baby. It seems to be a constant reminder that we set ourselves up for, and we often tell ourselves: "I'm aiming to be pregnant by Christmas" or "I'll have a baby by next Christmas." We set these goals for ourselves and when the big day comes it exacerbates our pain if we haven't achieved them. Another painful time is our due-date and the date we lost our baby which come around every year to remind us.

So, what can we do to cope with these days? It's important to acknowledge them for what they are and to be gentle with yourself. Speak to your partner about it in advance and let them know how you're feeling about it. They will be a great source of support and comfort for you. If you're spending Christmas with relatives, family or friends it's best to forewarn them that it's not going to be easy for you so they are aware and think carefully about what they say to you. It may even mean that you decide to spend the time alone or just with your partner, so you can just 'be' and relax or you may feel you want to be around your loved ones. Whatever you decide to do, make sure you're doing it for your own good and not to please others.

When we do things to please others and not ourselves, it takes up a lot of our energy and often leaves us feeling drained. I'm a huge advocate of doing things for our best interest or highest good. Women tend to be 'people pleasers' on the whole and consider everyone first before our selves. I feel that we need to be more selfish. By selfish, I mean to look after ourselves. It's not selfish in the egocentric, egotistic, inconsiderate way—more about looking after ourselves and being selfless towards our self. It's a form of self-love.

Using the old analogy of putting your oxygen mask on first, before helping others. It's a good thing to consider loving yourself and having self-love. Loving ourselves, doing what is right for our soul, our minds and our bodies. We are not only mind and body; our soul plays a big part and is often crying out to be loved and nurtured by us. Please, take care of your needs and feel good about doing it. Nurturing YOU in every way possible. I believe this plays a big part in our healing—that and forgiveness. Forgive yourself, forgive your body and forgive your mind for the gremlins that sometimes play a big part.

Sometimes it's easy to let the mind take over and it's not always healthy. The mind can go down a rabbit hole, a huge spiral going around and around where you tell yourself stories and begin to believe them. These are beliefs. Beliefs are something that we make up. We make up beliefs and we tend to tell ourselves things so that in the end we believe them. They become part of us, they are not healthy or conducive to living our best lives. Ask yourself, what story are you telling yourself and the world? Then ask, do I know this to be true? Mostly the answer is no. You then realise what you've been telling yourself is based purely on fiction—not fact. EAM (The Energy Alignment Method) is a wonderful way to release the stories that no longer serve you and put in a new one that will serve you.

Some common stories you may be telling yourself are:

- I can't hold a baby to full term.
- I'm not good enough to be a mother.
- I'm scared this will happen again.
- My body has let me down.
- I'm a failure because I had a miscarriage.
- I've let myself and my partner down.
- I'm too old to try again (this is common for women in their forties).

There are probably many more that you tell yourself. Please pause and say "do I know this to be 100% true?" Mostly it won't be 100% true—it's just a story. Let it go and reframe what you're thinking to be:

- I can easily hold a baby to full term.
- I have all that I need to be an awesome mother.
- I'm excited to be pregnant and carry my baby to full-term.
- My body is incredible in what it can do; mother nature is amazing.
- I am a success in all I do.
- My partner and I are proud of each other.
- My eggs are still good and viable; I can easily have a baby.

If you've heard of the Law of Attraction – there are many books on this subject from *The Secret* to *The Law of Attraction* by Esther and Jerry Hicks and many more – you'll know that what we think about, we are more likely to attract into our lives. So, if we are constantly thinking negative thoughts and worrying about things, that is the experience we will have. If we are able to turn around our thinking to more positive thoughts then we are more likely to be able to attract those positive things into our lives.

I had a huge breakthrough after I lost my first baby and went down my path of discovery about healing and alternative therapies. With the help of the self-development work I did, the books I read and the healers I came across I was able to let go of the negative belief and fear that I would lose another baby should I get pregnant again. So, my pregnancy was a positive experience in the main. I kept my focus on the good stuff and with the help of my healer, was able to release any worries that came up.

If you think you may not be able to do this yourself, I would urge you to get help of some sort. There are many therapies available to help you through the tough times and well worth the investment in yourself and your future child.

Conclusion

Having the right mindset when trying to get pregnant is definitely worth looking into. Why shouldn't we get pregnant well into our forties? We have heard of and seen people do it. I had my second child when I was forty-two and Cherie Blair (wife of ex-UK Prime Minister Tony Blair) had her fourth child at forty-five. It can be possible, and a lot of it is around your mindset. Believing and knowing and visioning that you can get pregnant is very powerful. It is mind over matter and letting go of your limiting beliefs, the beliefs that run riot in your mind, which do not serve us.

What if we could change those beliefs to believe anything we wanted to happen? What if we had a magic wand and could wish for anything we wanted? What if we could think bigger, live larger and do exactly what was in our heart? The only thing that stops us from doing what we've always wanted to do is our limiting beliefs. The stories we tell ourselves, the reasons we give ourselves to mainly keep us safe. You can decide to drop all of them and absolutely go for what you want to do. However, it doesn't happen by itself. We need to act and when we take positive, aligned, action the universe listens. The Law of Vibration (Action) is more powerful than the Law of Attraction because the Law of Attraction can't work without the Law of Vibration. The law of doing, setting things in motion and taking steps towards what we really want to achieve. Are you ready to get rid of the mind gremlins and go for what you want in life? It's not easy, but it is totally worth it to get the sunshine back in your life.

"Wherever the art of medicine is loved,
there is also a love of humanity."
— *Hippocrates*

Chapter 8: When the Unthinkable Happens

When we suspect something is not right with our pregnancy, perhaps there is a show of blood, or we have experienced pain or attended a scan in a clinic, our first call is to a doctor or the hospital. We are put into a system and have to work through this system. It can often feel like a machine, where we have no control and feel like we have to do as we are asked. It can be uncomfortable, frightening and we have a sense of powerlessness.

These are all emotions that keep us bound, small and intimidated. There really is nothing we can do, and we just go through the motions hoping we come through in one piece. It is one of the most frightening, experiences when you know there is a question about whether your baby is safe. We hope as we have never hoped before, that this is a bad dream, that we have perhaps imagined this has happened and we hope we will be told everything is fine and we can go home. This is where we often feel let down by the medical profession and where the medical profession can learn some lessons in how to handle women who have recently had or are having a miscarriage.

This is not a slamming of the NHS (this is the only experience I've had and most of the women I know are based in the UK), however, there are some stories that will curl your hair. Most of the midwives, doctors and medical staff are wonderful and do an amazing job, yet it is a job and they are often quite matter-of-fact about it in discussions. Showing more empathy would go a long way to improve a woman's experience.

The staff see hundreds of women who are in similar situations and therefore it is quite common for them, however, what they often don't remember is that it is a painful and unique experience for the person who is losing her baby. I've heard of women who have gone to A&E (Accident and Emergency) and were left sitting for hours before being attended to, while simultaneously miscarrying.

Women who have had or in the process of miscarrying are left to wait in the waiting room with pregnant women. These things can easily be tweaked to give the person a much less traumatic experience if only more care was taken. How easy would it be to take her to a side room to wait?

There are stories from women who have miscarried three months previously, only to receive a letter congratulating them on their pregnancy and asking them to contact the clinic to make an appointment for a check-up! It's something that the NHS could improve on as the systems are obviously not talking to each other. This leaves women feeling devastated and lost all over again. They have come so far in their healing, and making peace with what has happened and therefore it's another blow to deal with.

Mostly, women are told they are having a miscarriage and have three choices - to let it happen naturally, have a medical management, this means treatment with pills and/or vaginal tablets (pessaries) to start or speed up the process of a missed or incomplete miscarriage, or a D & C (Dilation and curettage procedure) a surgical procedure in which the cervix is dilated (expanded) so that the uterine lining (endometrium) can be scraped with a curette (spoon-shaped instrument) to relieve abnormal tissues. Women opt to have a D&C because they want it over with quickly rather than let it happen naturally, which can be painful with heavy bleeding and clots.

After they are sent home to either let it happen naturally, be medically managed or after surgical management they are literally done. There is not much backup care offered. In some situations, you can book to see your local doctor to be assessed. If you're worried about bleeding or pain you may have to go back to A&E or be referred to the hospital by your doctor. We go home and deal with it in the best way we can. Sometimes a leaflet for counselling is given. You feel like a huge yawning abyss has formed and you have to try and get through it. Luckily most women find inner-strength to do this. We are very good at burying deep and finding the strength to carry on as best we can. But we are mostly going through the motions, distant, confused and alone.

People's Experiences

Stacey told me she received this letter three months after her miscarriage...

The Health Visiting Service has recently been notified by the maternity department that you are pregnant. Health Visiting is a universal service available to all families with children under the age of five.

A health visitor would like to visit you at home before the birth of your baby.

Not only, did she get a letter, she also had a phone call—luckily, she was out, so they left a message on her answering machine. She told me how much it had set her back on her journey to recovery and how she had to pick up the pieces once again. A few months on from this experience, Stacey shared her good news that she was pregnant again! Nothing makes me happier to hear this news, I love to hear success stories.

Sara says:

"*After my second miscarriage was confirmed I was made to sit in a waiting room with happily pregnant women for nearly two hours, waiting to be seen by a second doctor. In the end, I left before I was seen, I couldn't handle it. Would sign a petition a hundred times to get things changed if I could. I would never want anyone to go through what I had to go through."*

Fiona says:

"I had the D&C procedure—cruelly called ERPC (evacuation of retained products of conception). Way to make a woman feel even worse than she does, NHS. Then I was put in a ward with pregnant women. Who in their right minds would do such a thoughtless thing??? But not for long because I made enough noise about that and ended up in a private room where I could stare at the wall and wonder what had just happened. Why had I been dismissed by the professionals? How could I have seen my baby less than 48 hours before and to be reassured that all was ok?"

How to Deal With It

When you are in a situation at the hospital, the best way to deal with it is to remember to breathe deeply and exhale deeply. When we are feeling anxious or panicky we tend to breathe quick, shallow breaths and this increases the carbon dioxide (CO_2) in our bodies, which can build up and make us feel light-headed and often unable to catch our breath. It's important to breathe out long, slow breaths hereby releasing the CO_2. It will steady your heart and make you feel calmer. Also, make sure you have water with you, and sip it periodically. Water helps our blood flow and therefore when we are in panic mode our body tends to shut down, so water can assist with blood circulation.

If you are in a situation where you've been put in a waiting area with happily pregnant women, and no one has realised that this isn't the best place for you to wait, take matters into your own hands by asking if there's another place you can wait. Sometimes staff are very busy and don't realise that this may be difficult for you.

At the end of the day, you may just have to get through it as best you can, knowing that this is temporary and you will be out of there soon. Try to keep yourself focused on your breathing and draw on your inner strength. You will surprise yourself how much inner strength you have when you dig deep at these times. Call in what you believe in, whether that is God, Jesus, Buddha, Allah, the Angels or the Universe, whatever gives your strength during your difficult times.

When you get back home you may want to feel a connection – have your community around you, your family, friends and partner – choose wisely here and choose those that you know will have your back. Join a miscarriage support group with others who have gone through the same experience. Most people find my miscarriage support group by searching on Facebook Miscarriage and Loss in Pregnancy Support https://m.facebook.com/groups/1274586595932991. There are lots out there, so go and find one where you feel supported. I try to maintain a positive, safe space for people in my group. A place where people can grieve, where they can rant, should they need to and a place where there is no judgement. It's also a group where we celebrate our wins, small and big. It's about feeling moments of joy and happiness and ultimately, it's celebrating a successful future pregnancy.

At this point you may decide to have counselling— again it's something that is helpful. To be able to off-load to a third party is useful. They have no judgement, they are not part of your inner circle and they are there to listen and be empathetic. Sometimes all you need is a listening ear and someone who gets what you're going through. This can be incredibly comforting and I would urge anyone to do it.

At the time of my loss, I had enrolled in pregnancy yoga. I called the yoga teacher to let her know I wouldn't be coming back. She was incredibly sympathetic and lovely and it was just what I needed to hear at the time.

I also connected with people in my circle I knew who had also lost babies. They were a great strength to me and were able to be empathetic because they knew exactly what I was going through. However, I found that it was often difficult for them to hear my story, as it brought up painful memories for them as well. I have found that even after my loss of twenty years ago and after all the work I've done on it, there are times that it comes up again and I feel the pain of the loss. Albeit, I can now say that I have a remarkable bounce-back ability and this was once not the case.

Working on yourself isn't easy, it's often painful, but through this process you will come out the other side feeling lighter, happier and when the bad times crop up (and they will) you can deal with them, and over time you'll discover that you too can bounce back much quicker to the old you! The key here is, to step out of your own way, to stop making excuses for what you can't do, whether that's because of lack of money or your fears about letting go.

There is a secondary gain to holding onto your grief, and sadness and depression because it keeps you safe. Ask yourself this? Do you want to stay this way in this state of worry and anxiety forever? Do you often wonder if there is more to life? If there is another way of being, feeling and living? If this is resonating with you, then you can start to make small inroads into feeling better. They don't have to cost anything. You have facilities around you that make a difference, which are free. By taking a walk in the fresh air you are changing your state of being, by having a bath or a shower or going for a swim. Stroke an animal, play with a dog and ball, stretch, breathe, laugh (watch a comedy), meet a friend, (one who always uplifts you), read a book, look at a YouTube video which will show you some yoga or a seven-minute tai chi session. All of which are free and fun.

Asherman's Syndrome

What is Asherman's Syndrome? Asherman's syndrome is scarring (adhesions) of the uterus. This scarring causes lighter periods, or no periods at all, and often infertility. I'm including it here so you can be aware of it and do your own research into it.

It mostly develops after a D&C or ERPC (evacuation of retained products of conception) or a retained placenta after birth and after a termination. It can also develop after a caesarean section or an operation to remove uterine fibroids or a pelvic infection.

If you suffer from scanty periods after having a procedure and are not able to get pregnant it would be worthwhile looking further into Asherman's. There is a treatment solution, and only a few doctors in the UK are skilled and experienced in treating it.

Check out the International Asherman's Association website (www.ashermans.org) for more information.

"I believe everything happens for a reason –
even if we are not wise enough to see it."

—*Oprah Winfrey*

Chapter 9: Moving Forward

Now that we've talked about your loss, your emotions, your coping mechanisms, your new healing strategies, your relationships with partners, friends and family, going back to work and what you can do that might help, this chapter is about hope and moving forward from where you were.

It's all about hope and reconciling with how you'd love your life to be despite your circumstances. It's about gaining some sort of clarity and understanding and acceptance.

For me, losing my babies is something that I'm (now) glad I experienced. It has made me stronger, more resilient, it has changed my life and I now know that I'm on the right path. I may not have gone into working as a holistic wellbeing therapist. This experience has guided me to my purpose in life and this book wouldn't be in your hands if it hadn't happened. It is something good, to have come out of something so sad. It was one of the benefits of my loss.

It is my hope that at some point in your life you will reach a place of understanding and I realise at the moment you may not be able to see a clear way forward and feel overwhelmed by your experience. Take it one step at a time, find the right support and you too can find your new personal power and start living your life again. Just believe that all will be well and that you will get through this awful time in your life.

When/If to Try For a Child Again

This is the big question that we all ask: When shall I try for a child again? I believe that some sort of healing has to take place before trying again because the area of the womb (sacral/pelvic area) will still be holding the energy of the previous pregnancy. We often tend to replace what we have lost and to replace it quickly. My advice here is to give yourself time to heal emotionally and energetically. If you're wondering how to heal energetically, there are many ways in which you can do this. Refer to **Chapter 3 – Supporting Self/ Self-Healing**. The way I work with women to help them heal energetically is by using The Energy Alignment Method. To me, it's the quickest way of releasing stuck energy from the sacrum and other areas. I have developed The Life After Miscarriage Transformational Healing Programme, to help with this process and get women back into alignment after such a loss. It's a journey, which takes women from grieving to conceiving and can be carried out online or in person. If this is speaking to you please don't hesitate to contact me for further information to see if it's right for you at info@life-after-miscarriage.com.

During the time I had my loss, I had many healing sessions with a healer and released much around my loss. It was instrumental in me moving onto the next step, trying again for another baby and is something I'd highly recommend.

Physically, it is possible to try as soon as you have your next period and I recently came across the following information in an article in the American publication, Romper, by Annamarya Scaccia:

"Maureen Cronin, Ava's chief medical officer (the US Fertility tracking bracelet) said in an email statement:

"The fact that doctors are still giving women inaccurate advice regarding the length of time to wait following a miscarriage to try again is particularly unfortunate given 67% of those we surveyed said they're eager to try again right away to get pregnant, is extremely unfortunate.'

Cronin added:

'Even worse, this advice may be hurting women's chances of conceiving another healthy pregnancy.

The World Health Organization (WHO) recommends that women who've experienced a miscarriage wait at least six months before trying to conceive again. But a 2010 study published in The British Medical Journal found that people who become pregnant within that six-month period — rather than after it — have the best chance of having a pregnancy that's healthy with the lowest rates of complications.

The authors did note in the study that, for women in developing countries, the WHO guidelines may still be appropriate because of the lack of accessible, quality medical care. But, overall, the recommendation to wait at least half a year before trying to conceive after a miscarriage may not be justifiable for most women, the researchers wrote in the study.'"

Finding Deeper Meaning for It

It's important not to beat yourself up about your loss. It has happened for a reason and we are often unsure of what that reason is. However, hindsight is a wonderful thing, and in time we can often conclude why it might have happened. The reason could be biological, simply that the cells were not forming correctly, which is what happens in most cases. However, I also believe there is another reason, one on a more spiritual level. What saddens me is, when women are seeking a reason, they often beat themselves up and form a belief that they were not going to be a good mother. Or if they have had an elective termination or abortions in the past, they blame themselves for any subsequent miscarriages. If this is you, turn that thought on its head, release the guilt around that and know that in all likelihood it doesn't have anything to do with why you miscarried. Look for a deeper meaning. Research suggests that those who have found meaning from their trauma or loss or keep a positive and hopeful view, such as Nelson Mandela when he was imprisoned for 27 years and Viktor Frankl, author of *Man's Search for Meaning*, fare better and heal quicker.

I was able to find my reason after working on myself and getting myself to a point of acceptance. Firstly, it occurred to me, after a few years, when I was lucky enough to have my second daughter, that the chances of still having her in my life were very slim. I only wanted two children and I feel it would have been highly unlikely to conceive a third successful time. What I'm trying to say here is that she, in all probability, wouldn't have been born. When I think of this, it pains me hugely. There's a reason she is in my life, to show love, to teach me and to challenge me and to hold up a mirror for me to be a better parent and person. I know that both of my children were sent to me for special reasons and are definitely meant to be here.

The second reason I have is that my first pregnancy loss, in all its sadness, was given to me as part of my journey. I know that I was put on earth to do something meaningful with my life, to make it a better place for a certain percentage of people. Those people are YOU. The women, who have lost their precious, loved and very much-wanted babies, who are grieving, sad and feeling alone and know that there is more to life. I went through my journey and learnt all I had to learn so I can help you. It was written in the stars, it was part of my soul contract and it's something I'm now thankful for.

Sometime after my loss, a friend came to visit and I remember her asking me if I knew about the Buddhist take on loss. I didn't, so she explained that the Buddhists believe a soul returns to earth to finish its soul contract and sometimes that only needs to be for a very short time. You see, the soul enters after a baby is conceived, after the first trimester when the brain has formed and maybe that soul didn't need to stay for long before completing the work it needed to do. It's an interesting thought and one that gave me comfort. In fact, my curiosity was piqued. I discovered some interesting books on past lives and souls. Two, in particular, were *Many Lives, Many Masters* by Dr Brian Weiss and *Destiny of Souls* by Dr Michael Newton. If you feel your curiosity also piqued, and you'd love to find out more, I'd highly recommend these books.

Goals and the Future/Your Purpose

Moving on and moving forward from a miscarriage and pregnancy loss is one of the hardest most difficult things to do. I understand this and empathise. I find there are two different types of people when it comes to moving on:

- Those who have their grief held close to them, not wanting to let go of it because they are afraid by doing so the memory of their much wanted and much-loved baby will be let go of, so they hold on ever so tightly to this feeling.

- The second group are those that grieve just as much as the first group, however, they realise they're holding on to this grief and realise that by holding on so tightly it's not doing them any good. They want to feel better, they want to move on with their lives and in doing so not forget their much-loved baby.

I think the main misconceptions I've found after working with lots of women is that they are afraid to let go of the emotion. Because they think by doing this they're letting go of their baby and they want to keep their baby close to them, around them and in their energy.

This is totally understandable and I get it, however, I do worry that this isn't healthy. I feel, holding on to these emotions of grief and loss isn't helpful. It wears you down and it's like carrying a huge burden on your shoulders. It numbs you, stops you feeling that life could be better and life can be better without having to forget your loss.

There is also a school of thought around grief, that it doesn't go away, it's still there within you, the love you felt for what you have lost, but your life gets bigger and grows around your grief enabling you to carry on and move forward and start living life fuller. According to Dr John Demartini, "There is always grief and relief around your loss, there is benefit and loss." Something we don't like to think about generally but I ask you to challenge yourself and see if there's relief, somewhere deep in your unconscious mind.

How would it feel to wake up in the morning and feel in your heart that it holds hope and is excited about the future! Imagine what that does for your energy; you'll feel lighter, happier, and you'll start to get the sunshine back in your life. You'll start to feel the possibilities that are available to you, whether that's conceiving again and increasing your family or drawing a line under it and deciding that life does go on but in a different way. Realising it's not the end of the world if you can't have children and finding other ways to fill that gap and to live your life with purpose.

Coach, Lesley Pyne, shared her story of being childless and how she overcame the feeling that this was the end of her life. She came to an understanding that there are benefits of not having children when she went out and lived her life on purpose, helping others in the same situation, sharing other people's inspirational stories and finally, writing a book so she can reach many millions of women in the same situation and give them hope, understanding and passion for what life can hold. Lesley's book is called *Finding Joy beyond Childlessness - Inspiring stories to guide you to a fulfilling life.*

If this is what you face right now, I'd highly recommend reading Lesley's book.

I share Carly's story here in that it may inspire you and you can find something that you can relate to. Carly came to me to help her heal and she's given me permission to share her story with you.

Carly's Story

I have had five miscarriages. I had my first fresh cycle round of IVF in 2011 when I was 35. It was successful and I saw a heartbeat on the screen at weeks six and seven, then at eight weeks there was no heartbeat. I had to have a procedure to remove everything (called an ERPC) a couple of weeks later. Two years later, when I was 37, I had another round of IVF and it was a mirror image of what happened the first time, except this time there was no procedure. The doctors told me to allow 'nature to take its course' and for my body to naturally miscarry (which was a traumatic event). Then in 2014 when I was 38 I fell pregnant naturally. Again, I saw a heartbeat on the screen at weeks six and seven, and at eight and at 9 weeks the heartbeat was gone. In the summer of 2016, I had a biochemical pregnancy. In January of 2017, I fell pregnant naturally. Two weeks later I miscarried. I am now 41.

The GP (General Practitioner) didn't support me until I'd had three miscarriages as they said that they couldn't properly investigate me until I'd had three. Unfortunately, this took me to the age of 40. I was sent to St Mary's Recurrent Miscarriage Clinic who said I had an abnormal thromboelastogram and that I had 'sticky blood'. They said that upon falling pregnant again I would simply need heparin and aspirin and I should be able to retain a pregnancy successfully. I had two further miscarriages after that. The follow-up care from the medical profession has been awful. I guess they are just doing their job and don't really 'care'. My friends have always been amazing. Most of them have had children in the time that I have been trying and always told me very early on when they found out that they were pregnant—to soften the blow, I guess.

The hardest thing about it for me is not having an absolute answer as to why this thing that is so easy for other people, is so hard for me. I know that in order to get answers I have to push and push. I know that the problem is with me, however, is it my eggs or is it my environment?

I feel that generally, the NHS don't care about women like me. I feel that IVF should be a free service for three rounds and shouldn't be discriminatory. That testing for recurrent miscarriages should be offered as standard. I could have easily fallen into a deep depression over my situation, which would have cost the NHS money anyway. In other countries, IVF is free or heavily subsidised. Everything about my journey has been difficult and it really shouldn't be. I work hard and pay my taxes so would have liked to have been looked after a bit better.

After many more tests I took upon myself to go to a private clinic, as I have finally concluded I just can't put myself through this anymore. My dream is to still become a mum and I have started adoption procedures.

Since this piece was written Carly has met a new partner and is now 30 weeks pregnant! Wonderful news and it seems when she took her focus off getting pregnant and onto trying for adoption was when she was able to let go and get pregnant. This is quite common and you hear of people who after years of fertility treatment, decide to adopt and then fall pregnant. I believe it is because they have relaxed, taken the focus off their situation and put their attention on a new outcome.

Whatever you decide to do about trying again or not, make sure you have thought it through and that it is in alignment for you. You know, deep within yourself, what is best for you, what you really want to do and when you have decided that this is the right decision for you.

I'm all for following your heart and doing what your heart desires. I'm also about listening to your inner voice, your intuition. Often, it's very easy to ignore our intuition, but when we get to the point when we know it's right for us to make another decision, (as Carly has done) we feel a sense of relief and inner knowing that it's right. We decided we just can't do it, can't take the heartbreak and disappointment any longer.

I speak to a lot of women who are in their early forties and they often have a mindset that they can't get pregnant because they are too old, that their eggs are not of good quality, that it just isn't going to happen for them or they are not 'meant' to be a mother. This is a fairly normal response, but I challenge you to change your mindset, to find another way both mentally and physically until the options are finally out and your eggs are truly not viable or it's not medically possible.

Mindset is just that! When you've made up your mind about something your mind is set. This can be either for the positive or the negative. If you have a mindset that you're in your forties and now you're too old to conceive—guess what's going to happen? Referring to the Law of Attraction again, when we constantly tell ourselves a story, we believe it's true and that is what we attract. Unless of course, you have had a medical diagnosis that you're unable to have another baby. I have heard of people who have had 'miracle babies' when they have been told they wouldn't be able to conceive.

However, if we tell ourselves a story that we believe is going to happen, it is more likely to happen. So how can we get ourselves to truly believe and embed our new, positive story?

- **Vision** – See it, write it and embed it into your energy. Your subconscious mind will process it and start believing it. Our subconscious (unconscious) mind is approximately 95% of our mind with 5% being our conscious mind. It is the conscious mind that rationalises, decides what is possible to do and what is not possible. Therefore, the limitations in your life are in part, limitations based on your conscious mind's critical appraisal of experience. The unconscious mind is the part of you where all your experiences and learnings are stored and this is what drives your behaviour. When we re-programme it to believe something else we can by-pass the old patterns and start to believe new patterns. This is where visualisation is so powerful; write it, feel it, smell it, experience it in any way you like.

- **Affirmations** – Write positive affirmations about what you would love the outcome to be. Absolutely believe that this is possible for you.

This is where EAM (Energy Alignment Method) fits really well. We can start to release the negative, thoughts, beliefs and patterns that no longer serve us from our energy, in five simple steps. See chapter 2 for the five steps. Once it has been released, we then bring in the positive affirmations about what we'd love to happen. Our chattering mind, our gremlins in the mind, often take over and start talking to us and with EAM we can notice when those thoughts are occurring and release them and re-wire our thinking by changing the neural pathways. Read more about the science in Yvette Taylor's (the creator of EAM) *The Energy Alignment Method Guide – The Ultimate Self-Help Book.*

I've also mentioned acupuncture and how it can help women get pregnant. My interview with Naava Carmen from The Fertility Support Company - www. fertilitysupport.co.uk, is printed below. Naava specialises in complex diseases in pregnancy and in autoimmune conditions, unexplained infertility, recurrent miscarriage, polycystic ovary syndrome (PCOS) and endometriosis. The preferred age she likes to work with are from 38 to 45-year-old women, so she can catch the multiple failed IVF clients.

How Can Acupuncture Help Women Who Have Had Miscarriages to Get Pregnant Again?

"The beauty of acupuncture is that it's evidence-based. There's evidence to show that acupuncture works not just on the spiritual and emotional side, but also on a concrete side which allows us to change hormone levels and see measurable differences in blood tests, to improve blood flow to the uterus at the right time and to make a difference to complex diseases of pregnancy. Miscarriage is half in the pregnancy and half in the fertility world, and you have to understand both of those things. Acupuncture works by understanding things in an integrated way. As a fertility specialist, I get as much information as possible from a Western medical point of view for my clients. They get blood tests, scans, information about operations, past medical history and I translate that into Chinese herbal medicine and treat them and retest them from a Western medicine point of view and expect there to be a difference. It's measurable from a Western medical point of view. As a specialist, I have a language of Western medicine and Chinese herbal medicine and can see when something has been missed."

How Does Acupuncture Work in the Body?

"When you enter the body in any way (even if you scratch yourself) you mobilise your body to heal. So, by entering the body with a needle we are making changes to all the systems, the endocrine system, the neurological system, the parasympathetic and

sympathetic systems, are all being accessed. When we put a needle in the body in a specific place the brain lights up and the message from the brain goes to that part of the body.

There are many interesting studies around IVF which show an increased success rate when you do whole-systems acupuncture, and by that, I mean three months of personalised traditional Chinese medicine treatment before the IVF cycle, and tailored support during the cycle itself. When looking around for someone to support you through miscarriage, you need to be looking for a fertility specialist, who understands what I've just talked about. Choose someone who can treat you for at least three cycles before you try to have an IVF cycle or you try to get pregnant, as when they do, my experience tells me that the outcome is completely different. We can also see that, amongst other techniques, there is evidence to show that when we use electroacupuncture (a special technique where we run a very specific electrical current through two needles on the abdomen), that we can stimulate ovulation. So, for women who miscarry due to a hormonal imbalance due to polycystic ovaries, we know that we can induce a better-quality ovulation earlier and that this has a knock-on effect on the progesterone levels, which in turn can help some women with miscarriage.

The other thing I do as a specialist is to focus on the immune system. It's a fairly new area and the immune system has a huge part to play in miscarriage and it encompasses an understanding of the different phases in the uterus—the proliferative and secretory phases. In Chinese medicine, this equates to yin and switching to yang within the different phases of the body. We can understand the different phases in the body and we can use Western medical testing again and take that information and work on the functions of organs in the body, as we need to.

We can break down the traditional Chinese medicine understanding of the immune system, into what is called a TH1 or a TH2 dominance. These relate to high natural killer cells or the profile of the person who has eczema, asthma or allergies. Both of those women might miscarry regularly, but their profile is different from a Western medical point of view and we can translate into Chinese medicine and treat them differently and expect to get a result.

The important thing to know is that acupuncture needs enough time to work. It's not like taking a drug, we need at least three cycles to work on a person before we expect to see a change. Sometimes that happens earlier and that's great but mostly we need our clients to understand from a Western point of view what happens in the body so they know why we need that time. Between the point when the body recruits a cohort of follicles in the ovary and maturing and developing them, one will emerge as the dominant follicle and will mature to a point when you ovulate and that whole process takes three cycles, so to treat for less than three cycles doesn't work well because we don't have enough time to change the internal environment to expect a different outcome.

My particular interest is women from 38-45, which naturally would have a higher rate of miscarriage anyway because of egg quality. Acupuncture works in changing the egg quality because we can change the environment in which those eggs are recruited and matured, and remeasure it by AMH (Anti-Müllerian hormone) and see changes as time goes on. Sometimes it's only half a point or a point, but that is often enough to make the difference between conceiving and not conceiving, making the difference of getting pregnant and staying pregnant. We also know from a Chinese medicine point of view, when the environment is right, the baby is healthier. For my clients who have recurrent miscarriages, when they're at the point of not having a baby, everything in their journey stops when they get pregnant. I look beyond that because, it's not just getting pregnant or staying pregnant, it's what the birth and the recovery are going to be like as well. It's an intimate connection with recurrent miscarriage between how well that embryo implants in the uterine lining and whether that woman has things like premature birth, intrauterine growth retardation, pre-eclampsia. They are all things we can work on in the months before someone conceives to improve the outcome."

How Does Weight Affect Getting Pregnant?

'Weight is the single biggest factor within our control that can change our reproductive health. By that, I mean waist circumference. If your waist is larger than it should be, it's an indication of how much adipose tissue you have. Adipose is the *same substance as cellulite but it sits around your middle. It sits on the top of your arms, under your chin and the thing I'm most concerned about it sits around the waist. It functions in a number of ways; it deregulates leptin and leptin regulates appetite. It's also a hormonal blocker and effects hormones being regulated and excreted, meaning that, for example, with endometriosis and a history of miscarriage there is a very highly inflammatory environment and bad oestrogen isn't excreted which need to happen to have an anti-inflammatory effect, and having a large waist circumference does not help with that issue either.*

The other factor is when you have adipose tissue it operates in a highly inflammable way, which effects egg quality because the eggs are sitting in an internal environment that is pro-inflammatory. One of the best ways to change egg quality when you are older, is to lose weight around the middle. Waist circumference, not overall body weight. We need to lose the brown fat (the bad fat), as every woman needs a little bit of squishiness to get pregnant. It's about understanding that difference and getting that right. A lot of what I do is support weight loss around the middle and I do that from a Chinese medicine point of view as well as a nutritional point of view. I have to support that secretion of the weight, so I clear damp, support Spleen Qi and release everything that is stuck around the middle in order to drop to the right sort of weight for each individual."

If you are struggling to get pregnant, then acupuncture may help. However, make sure the person you see has qualified in the way Naava has and specialises in fertility.

Holistic women's health therapist specialising in fertility, Rakhee Shah, recommends you look further than the medical profession when you're wanting to get pregnant again. She advocates the following:

"The excitement of seeing that positive on a pregnancy test, followed by the horrid sadness of losing your much-wanted baby can be a harrowing time for any couple. However, miscarriages happen for a number of reasons and none of which are your fault at all. It is the body's way of letting you know that the embryo potentially wasn't a viable one.

Miscarriages can happen for a number of reasons: poor egg quality, poor sperm quality (yes even though your partner got you pregnant), an underactive thyroid, low progesterone (often due to an underactive thyroid), poor circulation (cold hands and feet often contribute to the environment in the womb not being adequate), your immune system not working effectively (not just for fighting off colds and coughs) therefore attacking the embryo as it sees it as a foreign object.

What can you do to help yourself? The biggest thing you can do to help you back on the road of your conception journey is learning to let go of what has happened and put the fear right out of the mind and body. Holding on to grief can block the channels leading up to the womb and may prevent you from getting pregnant again as the body is under high emotional stress.

If miscarriages have been recurrent, I would strongly advise you to get your partner's sperm tested for with a detailed semen analysis to really ensure that nothing has been missed out, even if the NHS says all is okay.

Get your thyroid antibodies checked to make sure they are low. High antibodies attack the immune system which can prevent conception from taking place as the body is fighting something with a high-stress level in tow.

If you're someone who is always feeling cold, get your iron levels and thyroid checked but keep the feet warm at all times (yes even in the summer months) with cotton socks.

Nourish you and your partner with good nutritious healthy food to help build strong sperm and strong eggs. It has been said that sperm and eggs take ninety days to fully mature from the time they are created so what you have done in the last three months can depict the quality of both egg and sperm.

Holistic treatments such as fertility massage and fertility reflexology are brilliant therapies that can help tremendously at getting the body baby ready. They may help promote extra blood flow and oxygen to the reproductive areas, increase the quality of the eggs and sperm, and help with conditions like PCOS, endometriosis and fibroids to reduce so that they don't interfere with conception. They also help to nourish the liver and digestive health systems which are needed to be in good working order for conception.

Castor oil packs are a brilliant thing to do (only once all bleeding has stopped though). They not only allow you to have some much needed 'me' time but also help detoxify the liver, digestive and reproductive systems too.

The best thing you can do for yourself is to take each day as it comes, talk to your partner but also try to listen to what they need to say too, nurture and nourish yourself and make sure you grieve the whole process out. Please do not bottle it in as it can make the matter worse and really stop conception from happening."

Holistic Women's Health Therapist, Rakhee Shah (www.fbab.co.uk) specialising in fertility.

"Miscarriage can take a huge toll on a woman's body, not just physically but emotionally too. I have, like many of you, been there and dealt with the aftermath of losing several pregnancies. I did the best I could with the support that family and friends warmly offered. Many years later, I look back and I wish there had been more professional advice available and that miscarriage was as openly spoken about as it is now. So, thank you, Jo, for your putting the effort into writing this book and for the years you have invested in helping women get back on their feet after pregnancy loss. Well done!

In my thirties, while I was working in finance, which was very exciting but also incredibly stressful, my health started to suffer and at the same time I started losing pregnancies. At the time there was little in the way of functional medicine but, following some good advice, I took a career break, changed the way I ate, reduced stress to a bare minimum and focused on healing my body. Soon after that, I had my first child and now I am the proud mama of three wonderful children. All three pregnancies were firmly supported by changes in my diet and lifestyle alongside acupuncture as well as medical care.

After my career break, I decided to retrain and embarked on a nutritional therapy degree. Now I specialise in fertility and women's health to support women and couples prior to and during their fertility journey. I see many clients following miscarriages. I assess their nutritional needs and support their hormonal balance, but more often than not I refer them to an experienced therapist to help them deal with the trauma of what has just happened to them.

From a nutritional and functional medicine perspective, my aim is to ensure my clients have plenty of nutrients such as magnesium to support their hormones rebalancing since their body was getting ready to carry a pregnancy for several more months and suddenly, it isn't.

I recommend eating regularly as appetite tends to decrease as well as choosing foods that are easy to digest but nutrient dense at the same time such as broths, nut butters, energy balls, green smoothies and organic meats to replenish lost nutrients and help women regain their strength.

It is common to turn to comfort foods when recovering from any trauma, both physical or emotional, but highly processed foods are low in nutrients and can also negatively affect mood, as a result of their sugar content and additives, which will not support recovery. A much better option is to include the following in your diet: fresh wholesome foods like avocado, organic chicken, whole grains and pseudo-grains like quinoa, nuts and seeds, fresh fruit and vegetables and, of course, a little bit of dark chocolate every now and again! Gentle detoxing can be a good way to support the return to normal cycles and emotional healing. Plenty of fluids and fibre from whole grains, nuts, seeds, fruit and vegetables will help excrete excess hormones but the liver also needs to be looked after so those hormones can be excreted.

Foods rich in B vitamins like organic meats and whole grains can help upregulate the initial phase of liver detox, which gets the process started. But that's not all, plenty of fresh fruit and vegetables are also needed to provide antioxidants to zap any free-radicals coming out of the detoxing process. Brassicas like broccoli and cauliflower are rich in glucosinolates while onions and garlic contain sulphate that contributes to the second stage of liver detox when excess hormones are water soluble and can finally be excreted. And let's not forget about anthocyanins, those amazing antioxidants found in purple and bright coloured fruit and vegetables, like purple carrots, that also help your liver work more efficiently."

Pilar Manzanaro

Nutritional Therapist BCNH BANT CNHC

Conclusion

I hope this chapter has given you food for thought and inspiration about how you can move on from your miscarriage, find hope and some meaning and even joy. It is definitely worth checking out the work of an acupuncturist, a fertility coach and a nutritionist if you're struggling to get pregnant again. Once you release the heavy emotions of sadness and grief around your baby loss, you'll find you can see that life can be good, even great, once again. Once you are pregnant again, it's also very important to keep anxiety and worry at bay. I strongly recommend you see a therapist, healer, birthing coach, or have Reiki, hypnotherapy and aromatherapy treatments to keep yourself as calm and centred as you can. It's very important for you and your baby.

"We are only as strong as we are united,
as weak as we are divided."

— *J. K. Rowling*

Chapter 10: Inspirational Stories

I've included the following stories from real women I've either worked with or know personally, in the hope that something resonates with you and you feel less alone knowing that other women have gone through similar experiences. I also want to honour the babies of these strong, amazing women who have gone through one of the hardest times in their lives and thank them for their bravery in sharing their stories with you and the world.

"You are rooted deep within my soul,
a part of me forever.
In the deepest parts of my heart... there you are."

Melanie's Story

In November 2015 we lost our very much longed for baby, who we named Grace Rose to a missed miscarriage.

My pregnancy took us by surprise and being in our 40s, our new arrival was going to change our lives dramatically. From the moment I had my pregnancy confirmed I felt only love and a deep bond with Grace. It was instantaneous and a connection I continue to feel on a spiritual level between us today.

There are different types of miscarriage, some are over quickly and others are not. With a missed miscarriage your body is still full of pregnancy hormones as if everything is ticking along nicely.

In our case I started to bleed slightly coming up to 10 weeks. Fortunately, we had an ultrasound scan booked in the next day. It was only then we were told our longed-for baby Grace did not have a heartbeat.

For a moment time stood still as we held hands and gazed at our little one on the screen in front of us. We will always be grateful to the sonographer who was so kind and helped us understand what needed to happen next.

We left with our scan picture of Grace, which I treasure and it's a reminder that however short our time was together, she was right there with us.

We were booked in for another scan for ten days later to make absolutely sure that there wasn't a heartbeat. I had asked the doctor and nursing staff what to expect and they explained that everyone is different and we headed home to let nature take its course.

Five days later the miscarriage started with a vengeance. It was brutal and horrific with painful contractions and extreme blood loss that lasted on and off for days, with little respite. It was frightening and no one can prepare you for what may come. I had no choice but to surrender and allow my body to do what it needed to do.

Several days after the miscarriage began I birthed Grace at home. Our physical journey ended. And looking back, this is when our spiritual journey began.

So, with the next scan a couple of days away I was hopeful that this ordeal would be over. But the scan showed there was still tissue remaining which had to be removed immediately and I was booked in for emergency surgery.

At this point, I was heartbroken, totally depleted and exhausted. And my pregnancy hormones were still high as if everything was still OK. Once out of surgery I felt relief that finally this ordeal was over and I could begin to heal. But little did I realise it was just the beginning, whilst the physical recovery may be swift, the emotional trauma was not.

What do I do now?

In all the posts online and the information I was given, it focuses on the facts, procedures and what is likely to happen during your miscarriage. What I struggled to find was any sound advice on how to heal your body, mind and spirit in the coming days afterwards.

The Tommy's #miscourage campaign launched the weekend we had our first scan. It was a lifeline in the days and weeks afterwards.

What I found was a lack of information, guidance and support available to women and couples who are traumatised by loss, overwhelmed with grief and have no idea how to accept what has happened and rebuild their lives.

There is nothing we can do to bring our Grace Rose back to us, but we have always felt strongly about being honest and open about our loss, there is no shame in saying your baby died.

We decided very early on that we will do whatever we can to raise awareness and offer our support to others. My husband and brother-in-law took part in the Ride London bike ride last year to raise funds for Tommy's and for me what has helped me grieve and heal is to write.

So, over the last year or so I have been writing our story, along with what I have learned about grief and ways to help heal after a miscarriage. I have also been able to connect with others who have faced a similar loss to ours which is invaluable.

Whilst researching and learning more about the impact of early miscarriage there is a recurrent theme, we all want acknowledgement that our precious babies' matter. Every pregnancy is a potential brand-new life, regardless if the pregnancy lasted hours, days or weeks.

Our culture is very much to get on with things and keep on going. Miscarriage is deemed just one of those things, but actually many can be prevented. In my experience and for those that I have spoken to, there isn't a time limit on when things will get better or a day when you're finally over it. For me, I know I will never be over my loss; it is something I am learning to live with day-by-day.

Were your friends and family supportive?

People often don't know what to say or do.

We will always remember those who expressed their sorrow for our loss and acknowledged our grief and sadly those who did not. My whole life and outlook have changed since it has made me question everything.

Miscarriage is lonely and isolating so it is imperative to choose trusted people who will be there for you; who will show up, allow you to talk when you need to, get you out of the house and do nice soulful things to take care of you. People who can hold the space so you can grieve in your own way and find your way forward without judgement are the best to be around.

What is your advice for others going through a similar experience?

If you are trying to support a loved one suffering the loss of their miscarriage, in our experience and from talking to others this is what they need from you:

Say: I am so sorry for your loss.

Do: Give them a heartfelt hug.

Acknowledge: Their grief and their baby.

Respect: How they feel.

Talk: When they want to talk about everything that has happened.

Wait: Patiently for them to grieve and heal.

Be Mindful: Remember their due date and that special occasions and celebratory announcements are going to be tough and emotional times.

Our Grace Rose was due on Father's Day and will forever be in our hearts and never forgotten. She continues to be the light in our lives as we learn to live with her albeit in a very different way than we would ever have chosen.

Melanie is in the process of writing her book to help and inspire women through their loss of miscarriage. *Living with Amazing Grace: A Journey Through Grief, Healing and Transformation* by Melanie Mackie.

Julia's Story

It was seven years ago. I was 42, very happy to be pregnant and there was a big gap after my son and daughter, but I knew it would work. I felt good, I was at a healthy point in my life.

When I first went to the doctor and told her I thought I was pregnant she said, "Oh well, with women of your age it doesn't always work." I had done the test and thought I'm pregnant, so I thought it was a mean thing to say. It crossed my mind that I should be getting more help, as in previous pregnancies I was prescribed progesterone. She did give me a light dose of tablets. One day I felt some pain and felt a bit uncomfortable but nothing happened.

I was booked in for the 12-week scan which ended up being at 14 weeks and that was when the horror began. In hindsight, just before the scan, I didn't feel as pregnant as I had done prior to that. It was a hell of a shock. They were just looking and looking and looking and then they step out of the room and don't say anything to you. I'd had two healthy pregnancies before this and I just knew something was wrong. It was thought world had stopped at that moment.

After that, it was pretty matter of fact. I was given the option of letting it happen naturally or a termination via a D&C. We opted to go private because I wanted it to be over as quickly as possible. However, it was a very cold experience, all very matter of fact, done and dusted and then we were home and had to get on with it. I was asked what religion I was and if I wanted a burial, which shocked me as I just wasn't expecting that and it was so final.

Because I was just at 14 weeks, I was waiting for my scan before I told any of my family and friends, so it was a double blow that I had to tell them I was pregnant and now I wasn't. My mother called me a dark-horse when all I wanted was some support and kindness.

I felt incredibly low, 'done in' and wanted to go to bed and never get up. My thoughts were suicidal. A friend who had early miscarriages was there for me when she could be and I felt my husband wasn't there for me at the time. I guess it was his way of coping to go out and leave me. My friend told my husband to get a doctor as she was very worried about me. The doctor came and immediately prescribed antidepressants. This is what got me through. They numbed me and were the only way I coped with life as a mother, a wife and a businesswoman. I carried on regardless and didn't speak of it again.

It wasn't until I heard Jo speak of her story Jo, that it brought it up for me again and now I feel that it's really helped to talk about it.

Has it affected your relationship with your husband and family?

Yes, I have since divorced and I really feel that was a pivotal point in our marriage when I realised he wasn't there for me.

My family didn't really understand, they were a bit cross that I hadn't told them the news I was pregnant in the first place, but I was superstitious and wanted to wait for the all clear after the scan. It wasn't spoken of again, I guess they thought I was coping and was okay.

What was the hardest thing for you at the time?

It was when I got home and had my suicidal thoughts. The most traumatic thing was the scan.

What helped you heal?

The antidepressants were the only thing that got me through and with some family traumas and my divorce, I stayed on them until very recently.

In hindsight, would you have done anything differently?

Yes, I would have sought help and talked about it— either counselling or psychotherapy. It would have *been really helpful to have had someone who had also been through it who understood.*

Looking back, have you found any meaning?

Maybe I wasn't on my right path and it happened to highlight something for me to be a better person. Otherwise, I would have just been mum, wife and businesswoman. Sometimes I get guilty feelings about having had a cigarette that one day when I felt bad, but I know that wasn't the reason. I think it made me stronger: 'I survived that'. It planted some seeds that all was not well in my relationship. It wasn't the fairy-tale I thought it was.

Sara's Story

I've had three miscarriages in the last five years. Each feels harder to take than the one before. I feel kind of betrayed by my body.

Since the last one, I'm struggling to become pregnant again too, even though I've been trying a lot harder than I did after the previous two.

After the first miscarriage, I was so terrified of it happening again that I suffered a complete sexual block. I've done a lot of work and am able to enjoy sex again, but sometimes I still experience resistance and any sexual encounter has to be planned so that I can prepare myself mentally for it.

Sarah's Story

I was 36 in 2006. We had moved to the US in May and I was really keen to get pregnant as soon as possible.

We had one child already who was six and had been trying for about three years to have another without any luck. All that time, although we had been living in Russia, so life was fairly hectic and stressful. As soon as we moved I started investigating IVF treatment. I got pregnant with our first go and as you have a blood test to confirm, I knew that my 'numbers' weren't that high and weren't doubling every two days as they should be. I kept having blood tests to check and things seemed to be getting better however after three weeks I started bleeding. I went to the doctors and she booked me in for a scan. That's when they said there was no heartbeat.

Did you have any support from friends/family/GP or the hospital?

As we were living overseas I had no family nearby. I hardly had any close friends really as we had only lived there for about four months. My doctor was very supportive though.

What was the hardest thing for you at the time?

I think it took a while to sink in really. It had been so stressful having all the blood tests and not knowing if it was going to work or not that when I actually knew it hadn't worked I went and booked a holiday straight away. I felt like my chances of having another baby were slipping away. But I just wanted to try again as soon as possible.

What helped you heal?

I booked a holiday to Hawaii! The day I finally knew that it hadn't worked my husband and I went for a long walk and talked about it all. Counted my blessings that I had one healthy child.

Booked in for my next IVF which was successful and I went onto have twins!

Pam & Ben Gordon's Story

Finding a way after three miscarriages

We are very lucky in that our starting point was that we already had a child. Our daughter Beth was born in 2010 (six weeks early – but that's another story). So, we had been able to get pregnant with her quickly and although I was 39 when I had her, I was fit and healthy so expected when we tried for a second child to not have any problems.

We found it hard to get pregnant the second time as many people do, we were older and equally more tired from having a baby/toddler in our lives. But in spring 2012, when I was 41, we finally managed it. Three of the five mums in the NCT group I was close to were also pregnant or had just had a baby, so it felt lovely. We told family and friends at eight weeks as everything felt great.

I was at work coming up to 12 weeks (scan booked in for the following Tuesday) when suddenly all my pregnancy symptoms of nausea stopped. With Beth, they had eased off from 12 weeks, but not stopped completely. Looking back, I think knew something wasn't right. That weekend we went to London as we had tickets for the Olympics, so I have a great memory of having a lovely happy weekend.

But Monday morning was when the spotting started and the cramps. I live in Brighton and they have a specialist Early Pregnancy Unit, so I called them and they just advised to carry on as normal and come in for the booked scan the following day.

At 5 a.m. on a Tuesday morning, I miscarried our little Tom. I didn't 'see' him as he was like a huge kidney bean of foetal sac and small placenta. So, I don't know if he was a boy or girl, but Tom is how we like to think of him. What do you do with your baby at this stage? I just couldn't bring myself to flush him away. We put him in a plastic box and took him with us to the hospital. Thinking they might want to see/test—little did I know that nothing is ever done until you have at least three miscarriages.

My experience at the Royal Sussex Hospital (NHS) in Brighton was just awful (considering they are meant to be a specialist EPU). Everything from a receptionist being rude to us because we asked where the EPU was, door sign hidden, through to what seems to be NHS standard putting miscarrying women with pregnant earth mothers with hundreds of kids running around, while they sit there blooming, you and your baby are dying inside.

The doctor and ultrasound nurse were in training and didn't speak to me or address me during the whole scanning procedure—it was all an exercise for them. The doctor's review afterwards literally put her head on one side and said 'ah' - you can try again soon and there are leaflets outside and ushered us out. I know this is routine to them and the see it every day, but for us, it was our first time and just one of the worst days of our lives. If they'd cared it would have made such a difference.

I asked the doctor what we might do with the babies remains, she said she could take them and put them in with the clinical waste. Just awful, so we took him home. I couldn't deal with them. My husband took them and buried them on the Sussex Downs overlooking a beautiful view, which we often pass and think of him.

I did complain to the hospital and then with much anxiety still had to go back there again for the subsequent miscarriages where nothing had changed in the care or attitude.

How did I cope? I didn't. At the time I didn't even register I was grieving. I threw myself back into work thinking I was doing okay and thinking about trying for another baby.

We didn't get pregnant, so we went to a fertility clinic for tests and all was normal on both sides. So, we tried IUI, which is a hormonal boost and sperm planting inside as close to the egg and ovulation time as possible. On the third cycle of this, we got pregnant in spring 2013. It was going well and all seemed fine and then at 10 weeks I was away for work for a conference when the bleeding started and over the two days of this work conference, my baby bled away. I had no large foetal sac to see, I think they just disappeared in large blood clots over that time. I carried on working as I was the conference organiser—somehow I had my priorities wrong at that point and I just carried on working, when I should have left. After those two days, I went home, and I slept for three days. I was very ill which was probably an infection and I look back now and all the symptoms look like sepsis. Thank god I'm still here.

But that event was the turning point for me and I realised I needed to have some self-care. I was putting my life on hold, waiting to have another baby and equally not dealing with any grief. I was very unhappy at work and life and at the time I couldn't work out why. It took me another five months to leave my job, but I knew something had to change in my life.

Because these babies didn't 'exist' I didn't feel I had the right to grieve in the way you do for a person who had lived and you'd known. So, I wasn't grieving at all.

I was lucky in November 2013, I decided to resign from my job and take a couple of months out which turned into 12 months. For the first three months I just rested and slept, I couldn't 'do' anything but cry and sleep. The as spring came, I began to try to find a way back.

I found a great counsellor, after a couple of tries with the wrong ones. She was recommended by a friend, and she couldn't have been better. I had about 12 sessions with her and it was amazing to really let grief out with an independent person. As with all counselling you end up talking about a lot more than you go in for! But I wouldn't have moved forward without it.

I did a writing and an art class. I got a personal trainer to get me moving off the sofa and I just felt better and had more energy again.

What happened on the day of my last counselling session is that I found out I was pregnant again. A positive end, but unfortunately this baby didn't last either and I had my third miscarriage at eight weeks. A quick and natural one. It was very sad, but I was in a stronger place to let this one go.

My husband, Ben, has been very supportive throughout but copes and grieves in a very different way to me. I want to talk and often he doesn't (he has a farming background so very practical often about life and death). We've moved in and out of being close and distant over the last six years and I think it will continue like that, but I know that ultimately, we want to stay together and will try to find ways to communicate.

My family live some distance away and although initially supportive haven't really spoken about things in six years—they see me getting on with life and don't interfere.

With friends, people I thought would be there for me weren't and it does make you reevaluate your relationships as baby-loss does change you as a person, maybe not forever but I wasn't a 'fun' person to be around for a good two or three years. I could be there in body, but the spirit and 'mojo' wasn't there and you realise some friendships that you thought were deeper clearly weren't.

I did have lots of friends who were supportive in different ways. Jess doesn't live near me, but she still always remembers dates. Locally, the best people were Kate and Claudia.

Kate helped me with practical support: food and going for walks. She was also brilliant and suggested ways to remember the babies by.

Claudia made me talk. Not in a pushy way, but she's Italian so when she asked, how I was, and I answered, 'fine' she realised I wasn't and asked again, really you aren't are you? She listened and let me get it out without solution finding and without judgement.

So, I am now six years on from my first miscarriage and four years on from my last one. I don't have a happy ending. I had three miscarriages, but I didn't have anything to 'test', so they could only test me again after three and all my tests were fine.

In 2014, we decided to stop trying for another child. I couldn't face any more miscarriages and I felt my life was on hold, waiting to get pregnant, losing babies for three years.

That decision was grieving as well, moving on from plans of being a mother to another child. We are incredibly lucky, we have our daughter, Beth who we can move forward with.

It would have been great for her to have a brother or a sister, but she is a loved singleton who benefits from all our love and energy.

The things I used to get me through these awful years were:

- *Husband – trying to make it work and communicating if you can. We weren't perfect at it and still aren't.*

- Friends – some brilliant ones who supported and listened to me. I will be forever grateful to them.
- Counselling.
- Time-out and rest.
- Memorials – whatever it is that will help you. I wrote a card to my three babies (which I have kept in a little keepsake box). I wrote them on the day they were due to be born (my rough calculations).

I also wanted something physical to have. My friend suggested plants/trees etc (but I couldn't bear the thought that they might die as well).

So, I bought a piece of jewellery a seashell necklace with three little shells on it. It's for the loss and for the life I have. Three little babies gone, but also three in life, myself, my husband and my daughter.

I wear it on significant dates, but also sometimes when I'm a little sad and want to remember.

The grief has eased, and I am more fun to be around, but I am changed by the experiences. So, my message to anyone going through it is that it will get better, but it is your personal journey so give yourself time and whatever time you need is yours not on someone else's agenda.

Debbie's Story

Multiple Miscarriages

The blue line that tells you that you are pregnant is such a special moment. Even though I hadn't expected it to happen quite so quickly as I had just come off the pill! I was preparing for my third wedding in just three months but both my fiancé and I were so happy. My only concern was that my figure-hugging dress for the wedding might not fit but I knew it could be sorted. Off I went to the GP the next day and he said he would set up an early scan as I wasn't quite sure of my dates. So, at around eight weeks pregnant I went for my scan and there was our little bean with its heart beating and all looking good. The due date was confirmed, and they suggested because of my age getting a nuchal fold scan at around 12 weeks.

At 10 weeks I was starting to get concerned as I didn't feel sick, literally nothing. This hadn't been the case with my first two pregnancies. Then I started getting some tiny amounts of brown discharge, so I went to the doctors. She dismissed my fears saying that as I had a scan at eight weeks, all was fine and that every pregnancy was different.

Around two weeks later I was standing in the school playground waiting for my son when I suddenly felt a rush of fluid coming out of my body, I looked down and realised I was bleeding profusely. I grabbed my son and ran home, which luckily was around the corner. I was wearing white trousers which by the time I got back were drenched in blood. I called the GP who told me to call an ambulance. I called my husband to explain what was happening but by a stroke of luck happened to be turning the corner into our road. So, I jumped into the car and we dashed to the hospital. When I arrived, I was losing blood very fast and I don't remember much after that until I woke up in a hospital bed in a ward. I was told I had a haemorrhage and had lost the baby.

I was in a state of shock and couldn't quite believe it. The doctor then asked me a set of bizarre questions such as did I work with metals and had I got a thyroid problem. They tested my thyroid and found the level was too low and told me that was why I had lost the baby. That HCG levels are affected by the lack of thyroxine and that was the issue. I was put onto thyroxine and told after six months I should be fine. Unfortunately, during the D&C operation when I was haemorrhaging they displaced a disc in my back and I had to have spinal surgery shortly after the miscarriage.

I got pregnant again about a year later and lost the baby again at around eight weeks. We couldn't believe it, I hadn't had a scan at this point, so we tried to get on with things as best we could. We hadn't told anyone but then because I hadn't told anyone I was pregnant I then didn't have anyone to tell about the miscarriage.

I then got pregnant quite quickly for the third time and this time felt really sick! I had a nuchal scan booked and went along full of hope and not worried at all this time. But the consultant quickly turned the monitor away and told us the new the baby had died probably within the last few days due to its size and that I must go to the main hospital the next day. I had a D&C that day and we left the hospital feeling like our world had ended. Both of us so unsure how to handle what was happening and having to tell the children and family the baby had died.

In the midst of trying to deal with this and the loss, I was then surprised to get a call from the hospital a few days later telling me to come back in and bring someone with me. When we got there, they told me they had tested the foetus and that I had a molar baby. They explained this was an abnormal pregnancy where a non-viable fertilised egg implants in the uterus. In my case, two sperms had combined with my egg. I had very high levels of HGG because of this and therefore this is why I had been feeling so sick, in the back of my mind I had thought I might be expecting twins! The next part threw me, they explained this type of pregnancy can result in cancer and that I had a complete hydatidiform mole which gave me the risk of choriocarcinoma. I was told I had to have my HCG levels monitored until it was undetectable and if it didn't return to normal within three months I might need chemotherapy. They told me I must wait until it was normalised before trying to get pregnant again and that any subsequent pregnancy would result in me being checked again.

Once things returned to normal we tried again, and I got pregnant again and this time things seemed to progress well, then again around 10 weeks I miscarried spontaneously again. We were in shock and just couldn't believe this had happened yet again. I had to go back on the blood test programme for HCG again and was advised to wait another six months.

The toll this was taking on my body was immense. I was tired, had put on weight and generally felt unwell but I couldn't shake off the determination to have another child. It became like a mission. Once my levels were normal again we tried to conceive, and I got pregnant straight away. I felt sick, but I couldn't face having an eight-week scan so decided to wait. On Christmas Eve 2010 I woke up and could feel something wasn't right and I was bleeding.

It was snowing, and I knew I was around 12 weeks pregnant. We just went straight to the GP who sent me to another hospital to get a scan and when I arrived they told me the foetus had died. As I was bleeding they wouldn't do a D&C. They said nature would take its course. I met the most amazing nurse that day and she couldn't believe this was my fifth miscarriage and that no one had referred me for tests. I explained about the molar pregnancy and she concluded this was probably why I had got missed. She referred us for tests. We had blood tests and scans and my husband's sperm was tested.

I remember the day we went for the results so clearly. It was April 2011, I had just broken my arm and we sat in the 'infertility clinic' waiting to see the doctor. I sat there thinking I am not infertile I shouldn't be there, but they had no recurrent miscarriage clinic so that is where you have to go. The doctor explained to us I had a condition called antiphospholipid syndrome, which was an autoimmune condition, which can be triggered by a haemorrhage. I also had Lupus antibodies. That I kept miscarrying because my blood was too thick, and this was effectively starving the foetus of a blood supply. He explained that I would have to inject daily with Clexane if I got pregnant again. I had to bear in mind I was now approaching 43 and I looked him straight in the eye and said, "If you were me, what would you do?" He said the risks were high and that the risk of maternal death was 1 in 1000 and the risk of birth defects should be considered. He said he would support whatever decision I made but that I must consider the risks carefully.

I couldn't get my children out of my mind who were then 10 and 17. They needed me, and I just felt, despite the long road we had already travelled, I couldn't risk it. We drove home from the hospital in silence and it felt like the world had stopped. That the dream of having a child with a man who I knew would love and support me and my baby, something which I hadn't had with my first and second husband, was in tatters. When we got home I said to my husband I would understand if he wanted to leave. He didn't have a child of his own and he had found the whole experience very traumatic, too. Something, which I don't think people realise. I knew how desperate he was to have a child. He turned to me and said that at the end of the day it was me he wanted to be with, that a child would have been the icing on the cake, but that our relationship was all that mattered.

I think I have quite a positive outlook on life and coming to the realisation this was not going to happen was hard. I had never considered that having a baby was going to be an issue as I already had *two children, so coming to terms with everything was difficult. I didn't have any counselling and didn't really speak freely to anyone about it as most of my friends had completed their families and I wasn't in a circle of young mums. I remember feeling very isolated and grieved alone. I did open my heart to a reflexologist, only around three years ago, who had also gone through multiple miscarriages and she and I cried together which helped. I went for reflexology, as I thought it might help my thyroid problems and she just said spontaneously, are you grieving for someone, and that was it! I started talking about the miscarriages. In hindsight, I should have got help earlier, someone I could talk to freely and openly about my losses. I recommend anyone to find help as early as you can to speed up the healing process.*

I still think about the first baby I lost every April and wonder what they would have been like, how they would have grown up. It still feels like someone is missing and I think it will always feel like that. I think I have reached a place of acceptance and I think my husband has too. But this has happened over time, over several years and I think the love and bond we have with each other has supported us through. Family were kind and sympathised, but I don't think anyone really understands unless they have been through it.

Stacey's Story

We were trying for another baby, and as soon as I was pregnant I didn't feel right from the beginning. I've already got two little girls and both my pregnancies felt exactly the same. With this pregnancy, I kept thinking that something was wrong.

I asked to go for an early scan, the first couple of scans were fine, but when we got to the 10-week scan we were told that the baby had stopped growing two weeks before.

They wanted me to go home and wait for it to miscarry naturally. I didn't want this, once I knew the baby wasn't viable I wanted to have it removed as quickly as possible. I didn't think I could cope with knowing the baby was dead inside me. I went back to the hospital the next day, an emotional mess, and I insisted that I have a D&C. I was fitted in two days later when they realised I was in a terrible emotional state.

I wasn't asked if I wanted the remains. It all happened so fast, I didn't have time to process anything. The lack of information was diabolical, I wasn't told that my partner couldn't be with me, I was left waiting for hours, not knowing when I was to go for the operation, no one communicated anything to me. It felt like the worst day of my life and I was treated like a number. However, the nurses were brilliant, I couldn't fault them.

I found the aftercare totally lacking. There was no check-up afterwards, no phone call to see if I was alright after the operation and no counselling offered. My partner said he would come with me to counselling so we looked into it through our doctor's surgery and discovered that the criteria for grief counselling didn't include an unborn baby! I found this unbelievable, the whole process felt heartless.

When I posted on social media that I was 1 in 4 women who have lost babies, I was shocked by the number of people who commented that it had happened to them as well, (and I had no idea). It got me thinking and asking why miscarriage is such a taboo subject? Why do we keep quiet about it? It's not our fault it's happened to us!

As soon as you get your pregnancy test positive results back you start loving that baby and are excited to be bringing it into the world and even though I only carried it for 10 weeks, it was part of me, and part of our family.

Sometimes, I feel like you're forced to sweep it under the carpet and I don't want to ever forget but I feel like I was made to forget because of it being a taboo subject.

What I have noticed, from joining support groups, is that there is a different process around the pregnancy remains within each hospital and area and I strongly believe there should be one process for all.

We started trying again for another baby right after our loss and I felt a bit scared that we might lose again, so it was a bit half-hearted, but now, having had a bit of time to heal, it feels right.

I'm very fortunate to have two beautiful girls and they were my reason for living right after my miscarriage and I don't know if I'd have coped as well if I didn't have them. Sometimes you're made to feel a bit 'guilty' for grieving a loss of a child when you already have children.

I lost some really good friends when I lost my baby, people who I thought would have been there, weren't. There was a general consensus, I picked up on, that I should move on and it was old news and I should get on with it. I would have loved people to contact me, come to my front door and just let me cry or just let me know that they're there. It's what I would have done for anyone who had lost a baby.

It has taken me a while to get over it, but my two little girls keep me busy, so I have to carry on, for them.

The things that helped me get over it, were my daughters, my partner, and a visit to a medium. I was told that I'd have another baby and I found that really comforting.

I was lucky, my partner was amazing throughout, so supportive and loving, he helped me through it so much.

It's now 7 months on from my loss, and I'm excited to say I'm 22 weeks pregnant and feeling great! For anyone out there who is trying again, I hope this gives you inspiration that it can happen again.

Amy's Story

I've had two miscarriages. In the first pregnancy, I had an early private scan at seven weeks, there was no heartbeat detected. I felt really sad, but I took it quite pragmatically.

The doctor asked me if I wanted to have a medical management, at the time he didn't explain that they sometimes don't work. I bled for days afterwards and had another scan after three weeks, where they told me there wasn't a lot of blood and the bleeding would stop soon. However, I kept on bleeding very heavily and had to go to A&E and ended up having another operation. It was very traumatic.

I then fell pregnant soon after with my son and throughout my pregnancy I was anxious. I didn't feel very happy throughout, but it worked out well and my son was born perfectly.

I fell pregnant really quickly after my son was born, and had a scan at week 10, which was fine. At the 12-week scan, we found out we had a baby girl but they detected that there was an opening in her stomach. All the results looked good apart from that problem. There was a 90% chance it would resolve itself. I had an invasive procedure and it went well.

At week 15, I went in for another scan. My husband was abroad and my sister came with me. I saw on the scan that her kidneys had been compromised and the opening in the stomach was much bigger. We were told there was very little chance she would survive the birth and certainly wouldn't live once she was delivered.

We were advised that we should probably terminate the pregnancy so we took the sad decision to do that. We had an operation to take her out while I was unconscious and it went as well as it could have done under the circumstances. Afterwards, we decided to get away and go on holiday but I started bleeding again and had to go back into hospital and have another operation. I was so sad and devastated and exhausted by it.

I didn't want a burial, I wanted to be pregnant again and I looked for people to help me. I went to see, an acupuncturist, a nutritionist and a therapist and got myself physically and emotionally ready to get pregnant again. After nine months I succeeded and was pregnant again!

My partner was very sweet when I needed to talk about our loss and always wanted what was best for me. He was very understanding, but he didn't know what to do to make it better. However, he can't understand what I went through because it didn't happen to him on a physical level.

One thing that I found really hard to deal with, was when my friends would tell me their happy news that they were pregnant. Even though I was happy for them, it hurt so much. It's one of the hardest things to hear when you're grieving your own loss.

Something that helped was when I joined your Facebook group because I was surrounded by people going through a similar experience.

We went on holiday and that was wonderful. We were away when it was my due date and it really helped to be away as I wasn't sitting at home feeling sad.

It was hard that my family were living in another country. It was really hard for them too, they were so sensitive about what I was going through and cried with me, which was wonderful. However, I needed it to *be my grief and not to think about other feelings and how it would affect them.*

I feel that there is no reason why this loss happened. It was random, horrible and life is like that sometimes. I read, that if you lose a child in your second trimester, you feel the same grief as when you lose a baby at birth. It helped me, that someone said, "It's ok, and Its normal that you're so sad." When I read that, it was acknowledging that it's okay to feel so sad, and I don't think I was acknowledging how sad I was at the time.

I was able to talk about my story to many people and I think it's helped to raise awareness. I want to highlight my story because I feel it could help others, as I was helped by reading different people's stories.

Jane's Story

We'd just got married, I was 31 and we went on honeymoon and I got pregnant immediately. There was a faint blue line on the pregnancy test, but I didn't have any symptoms and I started bleeding so went we to A&E on New Year's Eve. They couldn't scan me then and they told me to come back in the morning.

The doctor told me to hope for the best, but prepare for the worst and I hated him for those words. I went back in the morning and there was no heartbeat. I was absolutely devastated. It was the last thing I was expecting and I was in shock.

We decided to try again straight away after my next period. I assumed that I would be okay the second time and it happened again. But at around five to seven weeks, the foetus wasn't developing.

We paid for private investigations after the second miscarriage and they said they couldn't see anything wrong and put me on progesterone. We tried another time, I got pregnant and had another scan the following month and again it hadn't progressed and there was no sign of pregnancy at all.

This third time was the worst. It was horrendous and I was so low. We had bought a new house and were packing to move and I couldn't do anything. Soon after we were invited to a wedding in Miami and had lots of fun; it was the first time I'd had fun in nine months.

We decided to give ourselves six months before trying again. This time it took five months to get pregnant again and we miscarried once more. This one didn't hit me as hard as the others because I didn't feel as pregnant. Immediately after this miscarriage I got pregnant with my daughter and it was a successful pregnancy.

What I've learnt is that you have to keep going and push through and you will get there. What was so upsetting the first time, was that I didn't know if I could have children. I had rationalised the losses because they were only a collection of cells that hadn't developed properly and it was the overall feeling that I wouldn't be a mother that upset me so much.

I remember looking for success stories to help me through and I read that most people got there in the end. The only thing I did differently when I actually got pregnant, was that I was less bothered. In the beginning, I was obsessed and focused entirely on getting pregnant.

When I got pregnant, we were on holiday and I was relaxed and having a great time.

My husband had been shouldering all my pain for two years and he was so relieved when I was able to carry to term.

I talked about my miscarriages from day one and I lent on my best friend heavily who was amazing as she's a GP and could provide the scientific facts. I had professional help after miscarriage two.

The single hardest thing for me was wondering if I was becoming a mother and I was very anxious about this.

I went to acupuncture to heal from the miscarriages and I went to the gym and got fit. I felt being fit and having a break were the things that helped.

I think you have to find ways of getting your anxiety and worry out.

In hindsight, I'd advise to give yourself time to enjoy being a couple and try and enjoy the freedom you have because once you have children you don't have as much time for each other.

Also, accept that getting pregnant is out of our control and a lot of modern-day women control a lot of our lives, how we work, what we eat and when we go to the gym. It really threw me when I didn't have control over this. I found it difficult that I couldn't do anything about it.

Fiona's Story

My husband and I, with our gorgeous two-year-old, were staying at my mum-in-law's cottage in the country. We had just had a 3D baby scan at 13-weeks pregnant and could see our baby! We also had the nail-biting invasive CVS test at a top hospital in London, due to my age. (I was 40 - an elderly primigravida!) We were having a mini break to recover. I was exhausted and had been bleeding over the past couple of weeks and worried about it. At the hospital, the same as the midwife at my GP's surgery, they were dismissive. "It happens to loads of women," they said. I wasn't sure. I had been pregnant in a previous relationship some years before and I remember bleeding before I had a miscarriage at about eight weeks. It felt ominously familiar.

The following day I started bleeding more and having pains and ran to the toilet. I called my husband as I miscarried our baby. I was sobbing so much I couldn't look, let alone bring myself to lift the poor baby out. I was numb with pain. My husband looked down the toilet and wailed in agony. I barely remember getting to the hospital or what we did with our son.

I had the D&C procedure cruelly called ERPC (evacuation of retained products of conception). Way to make a woman feel even worse than she does, NHS.

Then I was put in a ward with pregnant women. Who in their right minds would do such a thoughtless thing??? But not for long because I made enough noise and ended up in a private room where I could stare at the wall and wonder what had just happened. Why had I been dismissed by the professionals? How could I have seen my baby less than 48 hours before and to be reassured that all was ok? How???

I was released the following day and given a few leaflets about counselling and what to do after a miscarriage. I don't remember the content but I remember it being so un-emotive and certainly not written by anyone who had an iota of knowledge about losing a baby.

I didn't know how to be. I didn't want to have to reassure anyone I was okay. (I wasn't.) I didn't want to listen to the same old platitudes: "You're lucky you have one", "You can try again", "Plenty of time, you're healthy". Or worse, people who crossed the road because they didn't know what to say. It wasn't their fault that they didn't know, who was advising them? The same people who were advising me. No one.

Getting back to normal was me looking after friends' two-year-olds while they nursed their second children. Turn the knife. I had to go and cry in the toilets on several occasions. A couple of close friends knew, but I didn't want to not see them, so the pain continued as well as the anger and guilt. One by one all the postnatal gang who were such a big part of my life went onto have another child. Except for me. Why was I the only one who couldn't have another child? I couldn't stand being a victim, being the only one who was failing to have another baby, of feeling the pity in people's faces.

I got busy. I decided to bury myself into learning something new. A distraction would be good, I'd meet new people (and bury the pain).

Then my brother suddenly died. Everything else paled for a while and I was on autopilot until not long after I found out I was pregnant again. We were cautiously optimistic. Surely it couldn't happen again? An 11-week scan showed no heartbeat. We were in shock. I got on the conveyor belt of the NHS. I couldn't bear to miscarry at home. I had too much pain already.

The third time we were half expecting it, though the early nine-week scan gave cause for optimism. I felt bad for the scanning staff having to tell us. Feeling like we had to reassure them it wasn't their fault. Here we were again.

The gynaecologist we paid to see privately had suggested going on warfarin as it may have been a blood-clotting problem. It was never going to be a consideration. We had reached the end of the road.

The very sad thing is the absence of the human touch, the lack of somewhere to go, someone to speak to, a resource on hand, to help you feel 'normal', someone who understands. My husband and I had to muddle through, though at times we could barely speak to each other through the tears. Jo Tocher has this vital resource. I truly hope that every hospital and midwife unit in the country gets a copy of this book to hand out to the heartbroken parents who, so desperately need the support and to know they are not alone.

Daniella's Story

I had my first child in 2004. A little girl, with a mop of blond ringlets. I was a happy stay home mum in love with life.

It wasn't long before I fell pregnant again. I loved being pregnant and was excited to bring a new little life into the family unit. My partner had started a new job, which meant he was travelling to the US regularly.

My pregnancy was progressing beautifully. The scans and doctor's appointments were exciting and uncomplicated and my belly was growing and the baby was moving. Bliss.

It was January 2006. My eldest daughter and I were at home and my partner was in New York on business. I remember it being dark out, after 8 p.m. I went to the bathroom and something just didn't feel right. Too much fluid came out of me and my maternal instinct knew there was something amiss.

I called friends who lived nearby and they came straight over. One of them stayed at home with my sleeping baby girl and the other took me to the hospital to get checked out. I was expecting to be home that same evening but after examination, they realised that my water had broken and I was ordered to stay in the hospital so that they could keep an eye on me and check for infection.

My partner was called and he came straight back over on the next available flight. My mother-in-law came up from Wales to take care of my eldest and amidst having my uterus sewn up and having to stay flat on my back, I ended up in a hospital bed with little to do but read and wait for visiting hours.

The official survival age for a baby to survive outside of the womb is 24 weeks gestation. At this point, I was 22/3 weeks pregnant so I just had to hold on for a couple of days to ensure the baby's survival. I had really connected with the little life growing inside of me and was determined to bring this little life into our world.

Unfortunately, my body had other ideas and at 23 weeks I started contractions. They wheeled me into the delivery suite and my partner was called. Before I could deliver the baby, they had to remove the sutures which involved a doctor with his hands in me, removing the stitches in my uterus amidst contractions and gas and air. The experience was uncomfortable and an invasion of space, body and emotion. I disconnected on all these levels to get through the nightmare unfolding, knowing that the baby would not survive.

The doctor who was removing the stitches took what felt like forever. With my contractions speeding up, he was unable to find the last of the stitches and stood back while I delivered my baby. It was a boy.

The doctor went straight back in to find and remove the last stitch. He was in there for a long time before finally conceding that he was unable to find it and left me alone with a midwife and little bundle. It was quiet in the delivery room. I felt violated and traumatised and when asked if I wanted to hold the baby, I said no. I am not sure if he was alive or not. I believed at that moment that he was dead as it was so quiet and I felt so broken.

After that everything was a blur of meetings and sinking. We were invited to the hospital chapel to hold the baby and were encouraged to say our farewells. We spent some time with him in private, which allowed us to bond and let go. It sounds morbid but it was a great help. We chose a name for him: Sammi Christopher. Sammi after Dad's best friend who has passed away as a child and Christopher after my grandmother's brother who had drowned as a child. The hospital arranged for a funeral to take place. I wrote a letter to Sammi and we wrapped him in my favourite scarf.

Getting back to life after losing a child is tough. I have memories of lying on the sofa watching my daughter play with tears rolling down my cheeks. She would come over and wipe the tears from my face and continue playing. It was heart-breaking.

Having studied psychology, hypnotherapy and psychotherapy before the birth of my daughter in 2004, I discovered EFT (tapping) which helped me deal with the emotion surrounding the loss of my son. I was also fortunate enough to live near the London Buddhist Centre. They offered two-hour sessions once or twice a week, with childcare. We meditated for an hour and learned and discussed the principles of Buddhism for an hour. The bonding and healing from this was a life-saver.

I went on to discover and study NLP about two years later. This also contributed significantly to healing the remaining trauma.

*****

After reading through this book where we look at the pain of loss, your emotions, the wheel of grief, relationships with your loved one and your family and friends, going back to work and moving forward, it is my hope that something has resonated with your experience. I hope that you feel less alone after reading about my experience and those of others and that it has given you a feeling of inspiration with new ideas and solutions to work with.

It is my greatest hope you have something to take away and put into practice with some simple but effective strategies that may help. It may also be of help to understand what your coping strategies are, and therefore there may be more work for you to do around these.

Time really is the biggest healer of all and I know it's a well - used cliché. Just know, that in time, you begin to feel better, you begin to make peace with your loss and find your way. There will be bumps in the road and ups and downs, but with the self-healing strategies I've given you to use, hopefully, they won't be as regular.

You will find after using these healing strategies, that you begin to bounce back quicker, you no longer feel stuck in the same place. The key is to take time for yourself, honour how you feel and change the scene. Something as simple and easy as going for a walk will change your state and make you feel better.

When you feel yourself in a downward spiral of negative thought patterns, remember you can change your thoughts and in turn, you can change your world. Turn it on its head, look for positivity instead of negativity, take time out, watch a comedy, meditate and practice your breathing exercises.

This book will help those of you who have lost, but it will also be a wonderful gift for your close friends and family to read. They may be feeling at a loss about how to approach you and what to say and this will give them insight into what you're going through, so they can support you to a greater degree.

Mostly, know that you are not alone. There are others who have suffered as you are suffering. Take time to reach out to support groups and others in a similar situation. They will be your comfort and support. Alternatively, if you feel you need more tangible help and want to feel better, quicker do consider my Transformational Healing Programme for those who have lost babies during pregnancy. This programme will help you release your sadness and overwhelm and get you into a place of joy again, so you can move forward and become unstuck.

Be bold and speak about your loss—for it is of great importance to you. Don't let this incident be for nothing, swept under the carpet, while you keep quiet and carry on. Don't let society dictate to you that we should keep our problems to ourselves. It is healthy to talk, you have experienced a major trauma in your life and quite possibly are suffering from PTSD.

This is the time for change, we are beginning to speak up about many topics that have had a 'taboo' around them for many years. Mental health issues, caused by suppressing feelings and carrying a huge burden on our shoulders are slowly becoming less silent and more accepted and highlighted within our society.

Pregnancy Loss is now spoken of more. Many generations before us have suffered in silence for years. Two years ago the UK TV show Coronation Street had a storyline where the character Michelle (played expertly by Kym Marsh) lost her baby, women in their fifties, sixties, seventies and eighties were contacting Sands, Tommy's and other pregnancy loss organisations. It gave them permission to reach out and talk about their loss all those years ago. This saddens me; I can't begin to imagine what those women went through, not being able to talk about it and just having to get on with life.

This is not you. You have a voice and one that carries weight for you, your baby and for future generations. Let's leave a legacy together, one that is heard and reverberates around the world. One that inspires another, one that gives hope and meaning and understanding and empathy. Together we are stronger, we are silent no more. Our babies mattered your grief matters, this loss matters. You matter!

Once you have got to a place of understanding and acceptance, take time to reflect on what this experience has taught you, what you have learnt and how you're going to move forward and use the lessons well.

The Dalai Lama says: "When we meet real tragedy in life, we can react in two ways—either by losing hope and falling into self-destructive habits or by using the challenge to find our inner strength. Thanks to the teachings of Buddha, I have been able to take this the second way."

I hope you have been able to find your inner strength and that some of the teachings in this book, which I have learnt over the years, will inspire you to move forward into acceptance, and find hope and joy again. Whether you decide to try again for another baby or draw a line under it, you will know in your heart when the time is right. Listen to your intuition and be guided by it. A woman's intuition is her inner navigation system, a guiding light, which always knows the way.

Resources

I run a miscarriage and pregnancy loss support group on Facebook, which you are welcome to join should you feel you need some additional support to your family and friends. As discussed in Chapter 4, the relationships with family and friends can sometimes be awkward and in our group, you can be yourself:

https://www.facebook.com/groups/1274586595932991/requests/ Miscarriage and Loss in Pregnancy Support

I also run the Life After Miscarriage Transformational Programme which is available online (group programme) and on a one-to-one basis. This is for those that would love to work through their grief and go from grieving to conceiving in a supported programme where you come out the other end feeling positive about life and ready to move forward. If this speaks to you and you're exhausted and at a loss of trying to do it alone, then this would benefit you greatly.

Please email me at info@life-after-miscarriage.com for further information see: www.life-after-miscarriage.com

Other resources named in the book are:

Naava Carmen – The Fertility Support Company www.fertilitysupportcompany.co.uk

Yvette Taylor (the creator of EAM) – The Energy Alignment Method Guide – The Ultimate Self-Help Book

Candace Pert – Molecules of Emotion

Brené Brown – Daring Greatly

Robert Oexman, director of the Sleep to Live Institute

Dr Tim Pychyl, Professor of Psychology at Carleton University in Ottawa, Canada

Brian P. Moran and Michael Lennington – The 12 Week Year

Robert Emmons, University of California, Davis, leading gratitude researcher – How Practicing Gratitude Can Make You Happier

Robert Emmons, University of California, Davis, leading gratitude researcher – The Psychology of Gratitude

Dr John Demartini – www.drDemartini.com

Sarah McAllister – 5D Wellbeing – Designing your Life and Your Home for multi-dimensional health and happiness: www.fengshuiagency.com

Viktor Frankl – Man's Search for Meaning

David Hamilton – The Side Effects of Kindness

Dr Brian Weiss – Many Lives, Many Masters

Dr Michael Newton – Destiny of Souls

Michael Hartzel – International Spiritual Healer www.michaelhartzel.com

Lesley Pyne – Finding Joy beyond Childlessness - Inspiring Stories to Guide you to a Fulfilling Life

Article in Romper by Annamarya Scaccia, quoting Maureen Cronin, Ava's chief medical officer (the US Fertility tracking bracelet)

Jo Trewartha – www.freeyourmindsolutions.com

Rakhee Shah – Holistic Women's Health Therapist, specialising in fertility www.fbab.co.uk

Jacqui Tillyard – Celebrant www.yourspecialceremony.co.uk

Karen Shaw – Parenting Coach http://www.parentingmagic.co.uk/

Shelley J Whitehead, Relationship, Dating & Bereavement Expert –www.shelleywhitehead.com

Wendy Capewell, Relationship Specialist – www.yourrelationshipspecialist.co.uk

Club Soda – www.joinclubsoda.co.uk

Nutritional Therapist Specialising in Fertility – Pilar Manzanaro of Purple Carrot https://purplecarrotnutrition.co.uk/

International Asherman's Syndrome – (IAA) https://www.facebook.com/ashermans.syndrome/

Other books you may like to read about miscarriage and pregnancy loss are:

Living with Amazing Grace - a journey through grief, healing and transformation by Melanie Mackie www.melaniemackie.org

The Magical Unfolding – 8 Magical Processes for Peace, Potential & Purpose by Helen Rebello

Charities and Organisations that provide wonderful support and information in the UK:

www.sayinggoodbye.org

www.tommys.org

www.miscarriageassociation.org.uk

http://www.sands.org.uk/

http://genesisresearchtrust.com The largest collaboration of reproductive health research in the UK, investigating how and why things can go wrong in conception, pregnancy and birth.

Acknowledgements

The writing of this book wouldn't have happened without the inspiration, encouragement, loving suggestions, butt-kicking and pulling along from the following people.

My heartfelt thanks go to my husband Mo, and daughters Lilia and Hana, for their encouragement and acceptance of "I'm just going to write my book" and listening to the ups and downs along the way and lovingly wanting me to succeed and acknowledge our John's existence.

To my parents, Elizabeth and John Tocher, for showing me integrity and love and a strong work ethic.

To my sisters, Ginny and Rosie, for their quiet support and love from afar.

Thanks to Karen Shaw, Karen McCombie, Paula Carter and Shari Thompson for the walks, talks, advice and for sharing the sometimes painful 'birthing' of the book, and all those too many to name, who've cheered me on from the sidelines and encouraged me, one step at a time—you know who you are!

For those who sent loving support when I reached out in my EAM group of inspirational mentors, you know who you are.

Special thanks go to Karen Shaw, Sunita Koshal, Rae Antony, Pam Gordon and Fiona Whitfield who read and reviewed my book and encouraged me to continue and affirmed I was on the right track.

Many thanks to my mentor, Yvette Taylor, yvette@ energyalignmentmethod.com who without the Energy Alignment Method 10-month programme this book would have merely been a fleeting thought. Thanks for all the loving kick-aresery over the years and solid belief and love.

To Emily Gowor, who coached me through the entire project thank you for your insight, inspiration, belief and friendship and for gently pulling me along. It really wouldn't be here without you! To all my 'Retreat to Write' fellow authors: John, Kavitha, Jacqui, Suzanne, Gerry, Britt, Eileen and Kate, of course Mama Rae for feeding us with love. Many thanks for your input and encouragement, bonhomie and love.

This book wouldn't have so much heart and bravery if it weren't for the special people who shared their personal stories with me. Heartfelt thanks to Alex, Carly, Daniella, Debbie, Diana, Fiona, Gillian, Jane, Julia, Kerry, Melanie, Pam, Stacey, Sara, Sarah, Tina and the many others I've spoken to or worked with over the years.

Acknowledgements

Many thanks to all who contributed their expertise and therefore made the book more of a rounded guide: Shelley Whitehead, Wendy Capewell, Julie Tortora, Naava Carmen, Jo Trewartha, Renata Dosanjh, Karen Shaw, Jacqui Tillyard, Rakhee Shah and Pilar Manzanaro.

To Marina Gask, copywriter and journalist, for crafting the wording on the cover and generally having my best interests at heart, encouraging me to #bemoreaudrey.

To Nicola Wordsworth Brand Guardian, so many thanks for designing my logo and beautiful cover of this book and for unconsciously knowing that 'Life-After-Miscarriage' was in my original logo albeit unbeknown to us at the time. Your heart shines through your work and you seem to know what I want before I do. Your talent knows no bounds.

To my sisters at Sister Snog, whose love and support and encouragement re-ignited my passion for getting it finished and for the masterminding with Paula Gardner, Marina Gask and Natalie Guerin where many ideas were brainstormed.

To Judy Beytell, my wonderful friend who was there for me every step of the way when I had my pregnancy loss, whose calm presence and nursing background helped me get through one of the worst days of my life. For that, I will be eternally grateful. And for the love and support during my healing from Jacqs, Ursula, Amanda, Kerry, and Michelle.

Huge thanks and love to Michael Hartzel, Spiritual Healer extraordinaire, who helped me through my grieving and enabled me to get to a place of conceiving, through both pregnancies and to this day.

About the Author

Jo Tocher, transformational holistic therapist and coach, enables women to heal from the trauma of miscarriage and pregnancy loss.

She is the founder of the Life After Miscarriage Transformation Programme and is one of the first Energy Alignment Method mentors to train worldwide.

In Jo's 20 years of experience, she's worked with over 5,000 people and trained in 12 healing therapies to enable people to change their lives.

She's a co-author of Our Infinite Power to Heal and has written for Psychologies.co.uk. Her work has been in the national press and Huffington Post. She has been interviewed on a number of podcasts and radio interviews.

She's spoken on stage and worked alongside Yvette Taylor, creator of the Energy Alignment Method. She has worked in the iconic Sanctuary Spa, the Portland Hospital and clinics in Harley Street and Mayfair, London.

She crossed over from the corporate world to Holistic Therapies after experiencing a late pregnancy loss.

Jo is passionate about increasing support for women who've experienced miscarriage and pregnancy loss, so they can move forward and find hope, happiness and meaning again.

Jo is on a mission to enable millions of women to heal from the trauma of miscarriage and pregnancy loss.

Born in New Zealand, she now lives in London with her husband Mo, daughters Lilia and Hana and new addition Binkie (the smallest, sweetest dog) and their shy but very lovely cat Midnight.

Photo credit to:

Lucy Williams Photography
www.lucywilliamsphotography.co.uk

Hair and Make Up by:

Rachel Barclay
www.rachelbarclaymakeup.com

Would you love to transform your sadness after your pregnancy loss and get to a place of hope, acceptance and even joy?

Hi there!

I meet many women who have lost a baby during pregnancy and found themselves feeling adrift and alone. Having lost two babies, I know that feeling all too well.

That's why I created the Life After Miscarriage Transformational Healing Programme for women like you. Women who want to feel like themselves again. Women who want to grieve and move on to conceive.

During this six-month online group healing coaching programme, you can:

- Explore how your emotions are affecting everyday life, including relationships with your partner, friends and family.
- Share how you feel in a safe space, in the company of a group of women in similar situations, who understand what you are experiencing.
- Discover techniques to help you feel stronger and more able to cope.

Using the many healing strategies I've learnt over the years, I'll support you as you heal, transform and feel ready to conceive again.

If a group programme isn't for you, we can work one-to-one, online or in person – wherever you are.

It's time to stop carrying on as if nothing has happened – invest in your recovery.

Please visit www.life-after-miscarriage.com for more details. Or share your story with me via info@life-after-miscarriage.com or book a call https://calendly.com/jo-tocher/initial-chat.

With love and inspiration,
Jo Tocher,
Programme Founder

Life
After
Miscarriage

CPSIA information can be obtained
at www.ICGtesting.com
Printed in the USA
BVHW020211041021
618082BV00020B/1371